Dear Respected
Mx Jaishree Mariam
Happy Diwali
Kind Regards
Anita Sharma
25/10/10

LICENSE
to
LIVE

A Seeker's Journey to Greatness!

By

PRIYA KU

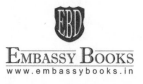

EMBASSY BOOKS
www.embassybooks.in

LICENSE *to* **LIVE**

By **PRIYA KUMAR**

© Priya Kumar
First Published in India: 2010

Published by:
EMBASSY BOOK DISTRIBUTORS
120, Great Western Building,
Maharashtra Chamber of Commerce Lane,
Fort, Mumbai-400 023, (India)
Tel : (+91-22) 22819546 / 32967415
email : info@embassybooks.in
Website: www.embassybooks.in

ISBN 13: 978-93-80227-48-1

Printed and Bound in India by
M/s. Decora Book Prints Pvt. Ltd., Mumbai

"You should build a better world," God said.

I questioned, "How?

This world is such a wondrous place.

So complicated now.

And I so small and useless am.

There's nothing I can do."

But God all kind and wise replied,

"Just build a better YOU!"

dedication

I dedicate this book to my parents, Kirti and Sona. My parents have the greatest hand in who I have become today. I owe every bit of my success to them.

When I was a child I often envied other children who seemed to have all that I did not. I was always acknowledging my lack in their abundance. It seemed to me that my parents did not let me have things easy. I had to earn everything that I got. It was not just money earned, but I had to earn my way through respect, through hard work, through a promise kept, through a problem solved and many times even through tears unshed. What I did not realize is that each time I earned my way to the top, I became a bigger person. It was not about the bicycle that I earned, it was about the promise that I had learnt to keep to deserve it. It was not about the new birthday dress, but about the respect I had learnt to exhibit for elders, to have them contribute towards my birthday present. And in achieving material abundance even as a child, I had become richer in ways that really mattered.

When people look at me in admiration, what they miss to see are the two pairs of hands that worked tirelessly in shaping who I am today. When people reciprocate the warmth that I have in my heart, what they miss seeing are the two hearts that forgot their own heartache to mend mine. Every time when people see a glimpse of greatness in all I do, what they miss to see are the endless hours of work and sleepless nights that my parents went through in keeping my world safe as

I grew. I live in a beautiful world because of the beauty my parents built within me. I am sane in the chaos around me because my parents very subtly nurtured values and integrity in me that have made me the success that I am.

My parents gave me the best that they had and nothing less. When I look back on all those years and even today in the present, I see two parents still working at their now grown up baby, doing the best they can to make sure I have a great life, and I do.

I dedicate my book to them. It's their talent and their wisdom, that speaks through mine.

Mom, Dad, I love you.

acknowledgement

The Universe is a collective whole. Without the planets revolving around it, the mighty sun would burn purposelessly. Without the sun burning with all its power, the planets would cease to exist with life. Everything is connected and fulfilling a larger purpose, a larger game in their unity. We too are connected in the same way.

Sometimes we do not see the connection and sometimes we don't plan the impact of our actions, but it would be a lie to believe and to live small, to think we don't matter. . . because we do.

There are so many people who have collectively added to making me what I am and to the work I do. I could not have made it here alone. There have been countless others who have supported me through their words, their actions, their blessings and even their intentions.

Even after a decade of leaving us, my grandparents' presence and pride is felt in every moment of my life. In writing the book I would often 'check with them' if my writing would do good for the world. This book is their acknowledgement.

My brother, Kapil, calls me a storyteller. Everything I say according to him, is a story. He saw talent in me from the day he was born I guess. On a stormy day when I would say, "The sun looks beautiful" he would slap his head and say, "You are a story teller!" I would swear to him that I could see the sun through the clouds and it looked beautiful. There WAS a sun behind the clouds and I could SEE it. And because I can see the Sun behind any cloud, I can write stories. "Kapil, thanks for seeing talent in me, I could see the sun behind the clouds but I missed seeing the sun within me."

My sister-in-law, Suchita, agrees with my brother and she is a fan of my stories. Her interest encourages me to tell more. And even before my manuscript was printed she wanted to get her hands on it to see how I could outdo the story I had just told her. Suchita has always supported me in any decision I took. She is the sister I never had and I am blessed to have her as a part of my family.

Aarya, my niece and my goddaughter, is me in action. She is the princess I wished I was. She has God eyes, she has a God smile and she is totally God in every way. When she holds my book with that look in her eyes, I know she does not need to read it to tell me that she understands and that I am appreciated. Aarya tugs at the child in me and urges me to return to the innocence I still have not lost.

Nigam Patel, my dearest friend, has had the biggest hand in making this book possible. His eagerness in supporting me without taking any credit or acknowledgement has made me a humbler person. He does not accept a thank you and sometimes I feel that even if I gathered all my good karma and banked it for him, it would still be less. I thank God for Nigam and the goodness he brings into my life and to that of so many others.

Pareen is all of 12 and she is the female version of Ronaldo. Her passion for football ignites mine for writing. Her commitment at such a young age is an inspiration for me. When I look at her, I come home and work harder. Shanaya is a doll I could play with and wish she would never grow up ! She is the cutest kid on the block. And their mom Jesal is a blessing to have raised such wonderful kids. I thank them all for bringing love and energy into my life.

Coco, my Yorkshire Terrier, was my constant companion through all the time that I wrote the book. She forced out of me the much needed 'love me' breaks where I had no option but to give in to Coco's 'pay-me-some-attention' growls. Coco makes my world go round and my mother suspects that if it weren't for the dog, I would not bother coming home.

All my friends have been a great, great support in all I do. I reckon even if I amounted to nothing, they would still be proud of me.

My publisher, Sohin Lakhani, has really been a great source of encouragement to me all through ever since we met for my first book. Nazlin aunty and Anu uncle empower me every single time we meet.

I also thank Priyanka Malde. She is a prodigy, a genius. All of 22, she helped me with the content editing of my book. Aarti's support throughout made it possible for me to write the book 'tension free'. Divya is my stress buster and I thank her for that.

A special thanks for Gisela Guenter and Karl Heinz for bringing me to this point of success. They have been my life coaches, literally for a very long time. They have spent endless hours in 'repairing' me when I was broken, in 'straightening me up' when I faltered, 'guiding me' when I was lost and above all they have helped me find my sanity and joy and success by becoming a better person with each passing day.

I would not have made it without my editors Sonavi Desai and Shabnam Lakhani for having done such a wonderful job with my words. They added the zing in my expression.

I thank my relatives who have really supported me with their blessings. Even though I am a very private person to the point of being a loner, they have understood and accepted my absence every time they meet. I thank my uncle Virendra for his good humour and wisdom and for keeping me connected with the family; if it weren't for him, I would be without one.

I cannot end the list without thanking all my fans and well-wishers. You will never know the joy that you have sent my way by your emails and letters and smses. I am encouraged, and this book is a result of that encouragement.

Eternally grateful,

Priya Kumar

Sonu Niigaam

The heart of your soul is felt each time you sing.
Your voice is not just for a song, but to complete the missing song in everyone's heart. Each time I hear you... the essence of your energy flows out from the speakers into my being, and I feel alive again, connected again, in love again.

You are blessed, and your energy is a blessing for all those you touch.

how to read this book...

License to Live is about knowing and living in the real world, which is a blend of the good and bad, the lost and the found, the sane and the consciously insane. It is about finding the direction you are destined to head in and creating the life of your dreams with all you know is right. It is about surviving people you don't understand, about solving situations you have no control over and still becoming a bigger and better person. License to Live is about finding your spirituality in your daily choices and decisions, about being your own teacher, listening to your own voice and discovering the eternal knowing that you have so well disguised under your fake helplessness.

I have taken many trips in my life. I am a professional traveller. Meeting people and learning from them is something I enjoy doing. License to Live has been a journey that I really never went on and so the story to follow is a work of fiction. Since this journey is so powerful that it changes the seeker's life, I decided to play the lead role in the story. That way I could actually 'live through' the experiences of the story.

It's like when you make your own movie, you can choose to play the role of a hero if you so desire. And since it's my book, the decision came easy. The plot was so beautiful that I wanted to be in the journey. I did not want to miss the opportunity of learning first hand what all the characters in the story sought to teach. So what if the journey was not real or true? Since I got to live it in the story, the journey is real for me now. If I have chosen to play the lead role, you too can play the lead role as you read this as your story. Priya, the corporate trainer, is me. The feelings expressed are truly mine. And as much as I have shared insights about Priya, the character, and searched her heart and bared her soul, I want to clarify that I never ran away from home, I never flunked my exams, I never slept with Ron and I still don't own a house ☺ !

What is really interesting to me is that through the journey of License to Live I have discovered that I know much more than I give myself credit for. I have always known that something was amiss in my life and in not knowing what it was, I had never found it. I have found my joy and my sanity in writing this book; I am hoping that in reading this book you will find rejoice in mine.

I could use your company in my journey towards greatness and if you are ready to go, let's roll!

contents

CHAPTER 1 /

On the Lonely Seaway

It had been a typical day, exactly the kind of day I had been living for so long. I felt weary and indifferent at the end of this rather long day as I had felt weary and indifferent at the start. I stood leaning against my car. The black BMW gleamed majestically in the golden rays of the setting sun. I held a newspaper in my hand as I stared blankly at the horizon. Huge waves crashed on the sea face spraying water but I looked on without a blink. 'A Corporate Trainer with a Difference' was a story a journalist had done a few days ago. I looked at my picture and sighed. The orange sun was about to disappear over the horizon and I clung on to it with my eyes, afraid of losing my only companion on the lonely seaway.

I was successful, or so I thought. I was pretty, or so men thought. I was smart but many others thought I was smarter. Everyone who did not know me thought I had a great life. All in all, I was exactly where I had wanted to be ten years ago. Now as I stood where I had wanted to be, something seemed amiss. Something that made me ask myself, 'What now?' Or rather, 'Where now?'

It's the same feeling a student has after the graduation he was so eagerly waiting for; 'now what?' It's the same emotion a new bride feels after the vows to the man she loves so dearly; 'is this it?' It's the same confusion a man feels after his promotion at work; 'is this success?'

I had a dream job. I was the owner and chief of my empire, my training company. I was good at what I did, I was famous, and I was rich. I had worked hard for seven long years and created a reality that had existed only in my dreams. Yet amongst all this achievement there was a void, a void that I could not understand. I knew something was missing but I did not know what.

Today that missing jigsaw piece was pulling me into a well of depression. Have you ever felt that something was missing in your life, even though there was nothing really wrong? Have you ever returned one evening from work feeling indifferent about your contribution and wondered, "Is this what I want to do for the rest of my life?" Have you ever been confused about what you really want? Have you ever felt lost when you were asked, "What would make you happy?" Have you ever in your life felt that you had no idea where your life was headed, even though the whole world thought you were on track? Today all these emotions came charging at me from every direction. I had been ignoring them for a long time but today I was cornered. I needed help. Priya Kumar, the corporate guru, didn't know where her life was headed! On the surface I was this wonder woman but underneath I was a little lost girl. For the first time in many years I told myself, "I need help!"

I began to walk towards the edge of the seaway. There was no traffic whatsoever. The low-lying bridge was under construction and not many cars took this route. I could see some construction workers in the distance, winding up their day. I could bet my life that being part of the seaway project made them feel useful. I could also bet that once the bridge was complete and their project was over, they would go back home as lost as I did every evening after work.

As I stood on the edge of the bridge, a wave crashed right at my feet and drenched me to the skin. Normally I would have taken delight in getting wet but today even the wave did not excite me. Another one roared toward me, lifted its head, and crashed right in my face but I stood like a rock rooted to the spot. I was drenched from head to toe in salt water. I knew that it would stain and shrivel my dark green linen suit but I didn't care. The sun had set, all traces of its existence now wiped clean from the sky.

I had had enough. I was wet and cold and even more miserable. I had come to the seashore for answers. I had come here in solitude to find some light and lessen my confusion and yet here I was again, going back with nothing other than a heavy heart. I could see another wave pulling up to reach me and as I quickly turned around I found myself bumping into a wall that seemed to have suddenly erected itself on the waterfront. I let out a yelp when I realized the wall was human. My first encounter with Kurt Rinck did what nothing had done to me in a long while—it shook me up!

I had stumbled onto the gigantic Kurt the way one bangs into a glass door. Except that this was a very fleshy door. Before my head dug into his wet chest, Kurt embraced me. "You are one rock of a woman," Kurt laughed as another wave crashed ashore and a violent spray of water washed over us.

I wiped the salt water off my face, straightened up, and wriggled out of Kurt's embrace. "I'm sorry," I said. I didn't know what else to say.

Kurt had obviously been standing behind me for a while because he was as drenched as I was. His black T-shirt was clinging tightly to his rotund form and I could see a very scanty hairline splayed across his head.

"A lonely road, a black BMW parked on the side, setting sun, crashing waves, a slender woman about to commit suicide . . . I could not resist the urge to pull up," Kurt raised his hands dramatically, explaining his presence. Such expressive communication with a stranger was rather uncanny. I sensed in that instant that Kurt was not an 'ordinary' person.

"Oh no, you got it wrong," I tried to get into my corporate guru shoes. "I come here often . . ." I started to protest, feeling a bit foolish. Damn, the man thought I was going to commit suicide!!! Heck no. I felt really stupid. This is what happens when you go to weird places to find solitude. Why can't people understand that it's ok to hang out alone? Why is it taboo? As for me, I enjoy my own company... . . er. . . is that what people mean when they say they are lonely?

"I come here often," I continued my protest.

"To find an answer to the question you haven't asked?" Kurt completed with a smirk.

"Kurt Rinck," he stretched out his hands grabbing mine in his. He held it the way a priest holds your hand in prayer. His car, a silver Jaguar, was parked behind mine, the chauffeur looking ahead into infinity. Kurt was really tall and he was sort of fat. A tall fat man. Balding head, ageing skin, he could pass off as slightly dangerous, the kind of man that could be a bouncer at a night club, except that he had the kindest blue eyes in the whole world.

"I'm Priya," I said. "And I come here often, really! I love the sea and the setting sun." I tried to cover up my confusion and did my best to look like I was in control. I tried to hide my emotional mess by making it sound as though I was here to admire nature's beauty in solitude. It sounded crazy enough, but not as crazy as Kurt's belief that I was going to commit suicide. I guess despite our pretence that all is well, people see right through us. Actions speak louder than words. And Kurt was sure on track with mine.

"If you are a regular here, then you must be really miserable." Kurt smacked my hand as he pulled me out of range of another huge wave that seemed to spill the entire sea onto the road.

We both walked towards the car. My teeth chattered as I shivered in the breeze. I had goose bumps all over. My hair hung in wet strands around my face. I was cold in the evening chill. "Would you like a towel?" Kurt asked, looking in my direction. "No thank you, I am fine," I said politely.

"That's good because I don't have a towel." Kurt laughed again. "You are a funny girl," he grinned. I forced out a smile. I didn't see the humor in his statement but smiled anyway. The journey from misery to happiness is a very long one. I could see Kurt's attempt to cheer me up and yet I could not find my way back to happiness. I had led myself way too far into being miserable and confused.

"So I am assuming you know the way home, Priya," Kurt said with a concern that moved me. He was smiling to make our encounter a light one and yet the hint of worry in his eyes revealed a very genuine heart

"Yes, of course, I'm good." I almost sounded like my confident self.

Kurt walked up to my car and opened the driver's door for me. "For the lady who will not be driven," he winked, "for she drives . . ." He let that sentence open for me to consider on my way home.

"And hey, if you ever need me, I am a phone call away," he said as he shut the door and waved goodbye. I nodded in acknowledgement as I started the engine and pumped the accelerator. I was just eager to get out of there. I swore I would never come and hang out alone and make a fool of myself. I was a corporate guru after all, and I could not be caught in a weak moment such as today. And I had no intention of calling Kurt, ever!

But wait a minute, how would I call him anyway? I didn't have his number!

I looked into the rearview mirror as the silver Jaguar made a turn on the bridge and grew smaller as it drove away from me. I was certainly not going to chase the man in order to get his number—he knew too much already.

CHAPTER 2 /

The Journey Begins

Kurt Rinck. The name kept ringing in my head like the chimes that persistently ring in the wind. The incident played itself out before my eyes as I drove back home. I was so preoccupied through the entire journey that I did not notice the distance I had travelled. I was surprised to find myself pulling up into my driveway, already home.

I got out of my car and slammed the door shut as my dogs came running out to greet me. My dogs are my salvation, always eager to cheer me up at the end of a tough day. Betty, the Spitz, was jumping about begging for the newspaper in my hand. I tossed it over in the garden for her to fetch. Coco, the little Yorkshire terrier, chased Betty as she ran for the newspaper. I laughed out loud looking at the dog circus as Betty came dashing towards me with the newspaper in her mouth. I could see my picture wet with her saliva as she dropped it at my feet to toss again. Coco caught up and began a tug of war. As Coco ran away with a portion of the newspaper, Betty stood at my feet wagging her tail in anticipation of the mutilated scrap of paper being tossed for her.

As I picked up the newspaper I did a double take. A familiar face caught my eye despite the darkness. I walked hurriedly towards the garden lamp to get a better look. I stared in disbelief. I was carrying the newspaper around with me all day and I had not seen this article. It was a big write-up, a few pages after mine: 'Kurt Rinck-Coaching for Success'. Could this be true? I must have been living in oblivion, not aware of what was happening around me. The man's article was right there and yet I had not seen it. I was so lost in my own circumstance that I had missed an important feature on a person from my industry who potentially was also my competition. It reminded me of the time my mother was looking for her reading glasses all over only to find that she was wearing them! Maybe my state of constant confusion was inherited but blaming my mother did not really brighten my life. I had not realized it but I had stopped living in the real world. There was no other explanation for missing this article. I had just met the man. This was definitely his face . . . I could hear my mother yelling in the house about the racket my dogs were making. My dogs were barking out in the garden, pulling at my pants, threatening to tear them, to get my attention, while my eyes were glued to the newspaper as I read on about Kurt in the dim garden lamp.

It seemed that the man was a genius in the industry. How come I had never heard of him? Actually that's the price of indifference! Some of us are so busy being busy that the whole world passes us by. I was so into feeling lost and confused that I had just stopped growing. I had stopped learning, exploring, and living. I did not read the newspaper except when it carried a feature on me. I had no time to read, to think, to reflect. I had no time for life. I had not realized this but in my whole drama of being wasted I had stopped living.

Kurt was conducting a seminar in India, in my city. That explained his presence here. Kurt was 44, German by birth but an American citizen.

His workshops were strange and unique and he was a 'ruthless' coach, the article said. He believed in results and guaranteed them to people he took under his wing. His methods of coaching were reported to be severe but seemed to work. My eyes raced over the article and I had to read it twice to make sense of it. I don't know if it was the excitement of getting to know a man who had touched my heart a few minutes ago or getting information about a suspected competitor. Whatever it was I found myself excited and alive.

After reading every word twice over I folded the newspaper and picking up Betty and Coco under each arm, headed for the house. My mother was still complaining; she was walking around clearing dishes and complaining to no one in particular because there was no one to listen. "Who are you talking to mom?" I teased her.

"Why do you ask?" she said, directing her frustration at me. "You don't have the time, and even if I say so, you . . . blah blah." I guess you can be a star for the world but at home you live the same life. It's the same mom for everyone. You could be the president of the country or a mafia don but the only person who can put you in your place is your mother.

I escaped the woman. It was always difficult getting past her because each time I came home she was ready with a barrage of complaints. It always frustrated me. I wanted to come home to some peace and quiet. Communication was my profession but when I came home I didn't want to communicate anymore. I preferred the company of my dogs—they did not need me to talk to them. My mother however did not buy into that logic and persevered with her case of me being irresponsible and uncaring, and sometimes I suspected she was right.

I ran up the stairs leaving Coco and Betty in the kitchen to dance around my mom. I rushed into my study and flipped open my laptop. I didn't know what had suddenly come over me but I had an agenda and it was called Kurt Rinck.

I frantically googled the website mentioned in the article and within three seconds a page opened up with a full-blown image of Kurt Rinck. He looked mean and stern, quite different from the man I had just met. I had been in his embrace a few minutes ago, I had been his concern a few minutes ago and yet the image seemed to give out sinister vibes. I shuddered, still cold in my soiled clothes.

The screen flashed the words...

'What if I tell you, you can change your life!

What if I tell you, I can show you how to create a life you have been wanting to live!

What if I tell you I can turn you around no matter how lost or beat you are!

What if I tell you that I guarantee you, you will!'

The words rolled out on the screen and headed straight for my heart.

This is what I was looking for, I thought to myself. This is where my answer lies. This is where I needed to go. I needed a change; I was lost and I needed to turn myself around. This was it. I jumped up, smiling with excitement.

I had not even browsed the entire website but within thirty seconds of reading the information I had made up my mind to attend the seminar. If I could only tell you all the impulsive purchases I have made in the past, I would be a millionaire just on returning the items I bought and never used. I bought clothes on impulse; I bought shoes on impulse. . . Heck, most of the things I bought were on impulse. After I bought the clothes I would realize I would have to wait months for an occasion to wear it, and when the occasion came, the clothes would not fit. In fact most of my life's decisions have been impulsive. I always felt the sting later when reality sank in after the deal was done or the love notes were exchanged. The same impulse made me gleefully decide that Kurt's seminar was what I 'needed'.

Kurt had a seven-day seminar in Mumbai. "I want to go," I heard the impulsive voice driving my hands as I clicked on the link that led to the seminar: **To enroll click here**. The page was bare with just those words. I clicked. The next page asked for all my contact details, which I excitedly punched in. Another page opened up with the words: **Are You Sure?** I clicked on **'Yes'**. At this point I was beginning to question my impulse. Kurt was over-selling it! He had me sold but now with his stupid registration process he was bringing me back to reality.

What kind of registration process is this? I thought. No details, where are the details? What will I learn? What will happen? Where is the summary? Where are the testimonials? Where is the write up? Tell me something!

The next page was the payment page asking for payment mode and details. "Hello!" I said aloud. "What am I paying for? What is the fee? This is crazy," I muttered.

Going by the reputations of both the newspaper and Kurt I knew this wouldn't be a scam. I had met the man after all.

I clicked **Continue** and my jaw dropped as the next page opened.

Course Fee $25,000. Press Continue to pay!

"$25,000!" I screamed. Is he out of his freaking mind?

I closed the window angrily.

"$25,000 !!!" I muttered, shaking my head. $25,000 is a lot of money to attend a seminar! Actually it's not a lot of money if you are buying a car or a diamond ring or renovating your house or giving to a charity, but it's a lot of money to pay for a seminar where you get no tangible product in return. If Kurt was giving an apartment free with his seminar, his fee would be justified but this was daylight robbery!

I opened the contact page and found a number. It was an American phone number and I decided to call. I checked my watch: it was daytime in America unless the man was in India with the American number.

I aggressively punched the numbers on my mobile phone as though that would help make things better. I have never understood my frustration! It just makes me turn up the volume of my emotions and actions and then later leaves me with more frustration and some newly added regret.

The phone rang at the other end and was answered at the first ring. Actually, to be honest, I was not prepared for this call. I was half hoping no one would answer so at least that way I had 'tried' to get some answers, though I wasn't really looking for any. I just needed to make that call to release my frustration. I was excited about joining the seminar and then Kurt had slammed the door shut on my excitement with this registration process.

"Hello." A man's stern voice answered at the other end. He sounded almost accusing.

"Umm, hello, my name is Priya and I was on Kurt Rinck's website," I spoke hesitatingly. I cleared my throat and continued, "I want to attend the seminar but there are no details about it. It just leads to the payment page and the payment is $25,000 and I don't know what I am paying for? So umm . . . could you . . . umm . . . explain please?" I felt really stupid and wanted to pretend the line was bad and hang up.

"The website clearly states the intention of the seminar in the first thirty second flash. Did you see that?" the voice spoke with a hint of arrogance.

"Er, yes, the one that says d*o you want to change your life and all.*" I tried to recollect what else it had said. "Is that all there is?" I now mellowed my voice hoping he would do the same.

"Yes, if you could change your life, that would be about all the change the world would need," he replied. Ohhhoooo, the man was intelligent, I thought. I must get someone like him to head my company.

"So is there no preview, no agenda, no course outline to this that I can see?" I enquired now with a little ease in my voice.

"Since the agenda is you, you already have a preview of your future and that's why this phone call. There obviously is no outline for the course of your life, else at this hour you would be preparing to sleep and not waking someone up to demand an explanation for seeking to change your life." The man spoke like God speaks from the heavens in the movies. I was stunned!

"Er. . ." I was at a loss for words. How can you argue with a man who sounds like God? "Er, isn't $25,000 a bit too much to charge for a seminar?" It sounded more of a complaint than a protest.

"How much money would you pay to turn your life around? How much money is a reasonable amount for you to pay to be happy and worthy of your own respect? How much time, life, and money are you losing standing on the edge of your potential being slapped by the waves? How much money would you pay to discover your answer within yourself? If there was a price to your life, what would you be worth, young lady?" I felt a chill as the voice barked through the earpiece and pierced my brain. "Well," I said trying to ignore his question and hoping to distract him with mine. "When is the seminar? What is the venue? It's not mentioned on the website."

"The seminar holding opportunities for you to change your life has been on since the time you were born. The venue is exactly where you are right now. If convenience of time and place is your concern then save your money and my time. I teach at my convenience of both time and place. If you want to change, it certainly can't be by your rules." The voice thundered.

"Are you Kurt?" I asked hesitatingly.

"I am not the answer to your question. The question is, are YOU Priya? Or are you short of your own worthiness? If you have the courage to meet yourself, follow the process and pay the price. For free you get the waves and waves talk, but you don't hear them because your hearing is impaired towards seeking the truth." God spoke and woke me up where I stood. With a loud click the line went dead.

He hung up! I was actually glad he hung up. I had nothing more to ask and he had said all he needed to. This had to be Kurt! No, I was convinced he was Kurt! How else would he know about the waves? The journalist was right, not only were his coaching methods severe but his pre-coaching methods were severe too. I could not believe this was the same man I had met at the seaway, or maybe he was not. He had not acknowledged his name after all.

My brain was working fast. The voice of God had shaken up and stirred my soul. The entire evening seemed surreal. What had I landed myself into? Everything that Kurt did and said and portrayed was right. This was exactly what I needed. I needed someone to help me see for real, what I had distanced myself from. I needed help, and I somehow knew only Kurt could do it. I was thick-skinned and fat-headed and even if the answer was around me it would be lost in confusion. I needed Kurt if I was to save myself from the disaster that I would soon surely create in my life.

I sat with my laptop on my favorite couch. I knew I was bigger than I gave myself credit for. Because I didn't realize the greatness in me, I lived small everyday and proved my fears right. Every now and then I would have a glimpse of my enormity in the words I would say or the impact that I would create as a result of my work. On the days that I was good I was invincible and on the days that I was bad I undid any good that I had done before that. In this to and fro journey from greatness to confusion I had always landed back on square one. One year after landing myself at the peak of my career, I was back to square one, and I was afraid that I would keep bringing myself back to square one year after year. I needed to move, and I needed to move NOW.

I scanned through Kurt's website a little longer. There was nothing much, except the same flash and the same payment. If someone found out that I paid $25,000 for a seminar they would laugh their heads off and I didn't want to be laughed at. It had not occurred to me earlier but for the longest time the fear of being ridiculed had stopped me from making the decisions I should have made. I started out in my career and became successful because I didn't listen to people but nowadays everyone's opinion seemed important and I found myself deeper in confusion. If you care to look closely around you, you will find that half the population is walking around confused and guiding others into a similar state.

I decided to sign up! This would be the craziest thing that I have ever done in my life. I was signing up for a seminar that was guaranteed to change my life for $25,000 and I had no clue how it would happen, when it would happen or where it would happen. I had bought my car for a $100,000 and it had not changed my life. I had bought many things for many hundreds of dollars and even though I had more things than I needed, possessing them did not make me a better person. Now I was buying a new lease of life. A new, better life for $25,000. A chance to change my life, to change my world, to discover new possibilities, to be happy, to be free. I could not believe I was actually my own salesperson selling myself a new improved me!!!!

With new vigor and determination, I punched in my credit card details. Before the payment was processed, a page opened and the following words flashed one by one:

This payment is for YOUR life . . . And may you never be the SAME again!!!

The page disappeared as quickly as it had come, and a message flashed: **Your payment is processed**.

My phone, which was on the table, beeped with a text message.

Thank you for enrolling for the seminar. Your reporting time is tomorrow at 4.32 a.m. at the Taj Villas, Mumbai. If you are on time, consider yourself late. ~ Kurt Rinck.

Tomorrow??? Oh man, the guy was crazy. 4.32 a.m!!! What kind of time was 4.32 a.m.? Who starts a seminar at 4.32 a.m.? Luckily I had a ten day break from work else my $25,000 would have gone down the drain in an instant. I had not expected it to start before a week or so. I found my usual cynical, frustrated self speak up. Grrrrr. I had just paid for the seminar. Why was I still fighting it? Who was there to fight with except me? It was already 10 p.m. I needed to hurry and get to bed.

Suddenly I could see myself doing what my mother does; fight and complain to no one at all. I needed to stop this. I wanted to change but I wanted to change my way! But how could I ever change that way?? I had put my money on Kurt and even after doing that, I wanted to call the shots.

I had not yet started on the seminar but I could see myself a little more clearly now. I was stubborn and I was stuck. I was lost because I refused to move or see the way. There was certainly a way. There was always a way. But I did not want to see it. I shuddered as this reality unfolded in front of my eyes. And because I saw it, I knew I wanted to change it.

I had paid $25,000 for myself and I could catch every thought in my head, question it and turn it around. If this was the impact in a few minutes of signing up then I could only eagerly wait to meet a new me after seven days. As for now, I needed to sleep to get to the damn seminar at 4.32 a.m. and I had to be there early because if I was on time, I would be considered to be late.

With no appetite for food, I shut down my world. I set the alarm for a few hours of sleep. I could not wait to see the man; the priestly terror to whom I would surrender my life in the hope that I would never be the same again.

CHAPTER 3 /

Day One with Kurt

The night was a disaster. I could not sleep at all for fear of being late. My mind kept tab of every hour that went by. It was almost as if I did not trust myself to wake up.

It was still 3 a.m. when I decided to be early, way early. I got dressed and left a note for my mother. I knew there would be a new list of complaints when I got home but since it would be a new me coming home, I would find a new way to handle her. I was already happier. The stars were up when I pulled my car out of the driveway. My dogs came out sleepily. I petted them and shooed them off to sleep, which they obediently did. It's easy having two dogs, get the older one to do something and the younger one will follow.

It was a beautiful drive to the Taj Villas; a ride that would normally have taken me two hours was spanned in less than twenty minutes. I guess that is the beauty of life. If we just reduce the traffic in our heads and hearts, success is within reach. If we allow the traffic of mis-arranged emotions to create clutter in our heads, then the twenty-minute ride can sometimes take twenty years to complete. We realize too late that success was only an arm's length away.

I already liked the feel of this seminar; it was doing me good, in an inexplicable way.

I arrived at the Taj Villas, whose property extends over almost two hundred acres. They have some of the most stunning beachfront villas in town. What an ideal place to hold a seminar, I thought.

It was only five minutes past 4.00 a.m. when I headed for the reception. A large lady in a black uniform started to walk towards me. She was young, average looking, fat, and her skirt was so tight that it looked like it could rip apart with any step. She came towards me and spoke in a South Indian accent, "You are here for Mr. Rinck's seminar?"

"Yes, I paid for it," I nodded. The reference to the payment was quite unnecessary but now it was too late to take back the words. Veni, as her name tag read, asked me to follow her as she started walking away from me down a little hallway. I found this a little rude and strange. For $25,000 I was expecting a grand welcome, maybe a glass of champagne, the red carpet rolled out. I had paid $25,000 after all. Some sexy hosts would have been welcome, guys preferably. But no such luck. Here was a solemn looking, unshapely, ordinary girl. She shook my belief in how an expensive seminar should be conducted.

Veni took me into the corner of a fancy corridor where there was a table and two chairs arranged in an interview-like fashion. Maybe it's a personalized registration process, I thought. Veni sat down and beckoned me to sit as she checked her watch for the time. She glanced at a sheet that had all my details and gave me a form to fill out. It was a basic form—personal and professional details. I was glad I had carried my passport, which I had to submit as proof of identity.

"Mr. Rinck has not yet woken up. We are missing one volunteer. The participants have started to arrive. Would you like to volunteer?" Veni asked, almost begging.

Now this is too much, I thought to myself. First the man charges me $25,000 for an insane seminar and now his assistant wants me to work for him too! I came here to learn, not to work. Instead of offering me some coffee, making me comfortable, showing me around, and giving me the inside scoop on the seminar, she was asking me to assist her. I was a reputed corporate guru after all. If a reporter saw me here, working as a receptionist, it would ruin my reputation. My old me began to do the 'old me' number. But wait a minute, whatever happened to the wisdom that I had signed up for? Was I so big that a little ordinary work was too beneath me? Haven't all legendary people gotten down with the broom to clean up their act and other people's as well? Was it really so shameful for me to lend a hand here?

"Yes, I can help. I'm here early so I might as well be useful," I said with a sleepy croak in my voice.

Veni was delighted. "Great, please go to villa 243. Kurt is there. He needs to be woken up. He usually leaves instructions at the door for the person who wakes him up. Please follow the instructions. I will see you back at the reception," she said, getting up.

Now this was already getting interesting. Kurt Rinck had overslept for his own seminar. The allotted time was less than fifteen minutes away and the man needed to be woken up! But why could Veni not wake him up herself? Why was she telling me to do this very sensitive task? Waking someone up is a very personal thing. I found that a little odd but I guess by now everything about Kurt's seminar was very odd. Nothing had been normal since the first instant that I had met him.

A sign pointed to the villas from 240-250 on the right. A little pebbled pathway headed in the direction of the beach. The open expanse was beautiful. It was dark and the path was lit by little lamps, half immersed in the bushes, on either side. Villa 243 was a beautiful one overlooking the beach. I reached the entrance and saw an envelope at the doorstep. I opened it to find a handwritten note.

"Bark like a dog to wake me up. You will know I am up when you see the lights on upstairs." ~ Kurt Rinck.

Bark like a dog? Was he crazy? The man was late and he wanted me to bark like a dog? There was a doorbell here! Why couldn't I ring that? Why couldn't I just call him? Or shout his name? Or throw pebbles? Or even better, open the door and pull his sheet off and get him to jump out of bed, the way my mother wakes me up every morning?

I could now see why Veni wanted to pass on the task of waking up Kurt to someone else. Bark like a dog, my foot! I had half a mind to ring the doorbell and make it sound like a fire engine on duty till the man woke up.

I had a hundred ideas in my head about how to wake up the Success Coach but he wanted me to bark like a dog. I looked around and I could see the butler scurrying away in the distance. I have grown up with dogs but I have never barked like one in public. But I would do it. I took a deep breath. I opened my mouth to bark but only ended up laughing. I tried again and let out a howl; it was hideous. The waves of the sea were drowning my voice. I looked around nervously in case someone was watching. I cupped my hands and started to howl but the fat man was clearly deaf or fast asleep. I decided to go one more time and let out the most pitiful bark ever. To my delight the lights came on and a fat man came to the window. I could not see his face but I knew it was Kurt.

"Get ready, you are late! Hurry!" I said, as I waved my hand.

The man slammed the window shut, obviously realizing he had overslept.

"Do you want me to send some coffee?" I decided to humor him as I broke into a run. I guessed if I was here waking up Kurt at 4:25 a.m., I was not likely to be late for the 4:32 a.m. seminar. I ran back to the registration desk, which was too quiet for a seminar. Veni was waiting for me and seemed in a rush. "You woke him up?" I was amazed that she seemed surprised!

"Yes," I said. Wasn't I supposed to wake him up?

"You are going to be late." She looked worried. "The seminar arrangement is five hundred meters from here by the beach over there," she pointed at a very far 'over there'!

"No way," I almost shouted as I ran in the direction of over there. I had three minutes before I was on time to be late. I ran with all my might. Kurt could be late but we couldn't? That was not fair. After all, I was late waking him up. This man was really crazy. My feet raced in the direction Veni had pointed out.

The question, I guess, was not who else did not keep time or did not keep their word or did not succeed. The real question was, were you in time? Did you keep your word? Did you succeed? So many times we make other peoples mediocre behavior an excuse for our own. So just because Kurt was going to be late, somehow it was ok for me to be late too. The point, not to miss, was that I was not Kurt and I was not here to do what Kurt did. I was here for my own purpose and I could not be late for that.

The beach was in sight and my sprint practice had come to some good use both physically and mentally. I saw a small enclosed area, sort of like an arena strung out on the beach. Some lamps were dancing on the rope that ran around the enclosure. There were three stumps like stools placed on the inside on the sand. A large man was standing at the shoreline, barefoot, with his back to me. "Kurt Rinck," I gasped. How could it be? I was just at his villa, waking the man up!

I reached the 'seminar area' and looked at my watch. I was two minutes early. That one-minute run seemed like a year to me!

A middle-aged man and a girl ran in behind me. Kurt stood there about thirty feet away, still facing the sea, his back to us. The setting of the seminar was beautiful. There was a string fence around three wooden stools. On that string hung earthen lamps with candles burning inside them. I looked at the girl who had come in behind me. She, like me, was out of breath.

"I'm Uma," she said, still trying to catch her breath. "I'm Priya," I forced out a smile.

"Karlos," said the man who looked like he was going to have a heart attack. He was not only middle-aged, he was also fat. He had obviously not run in many years. Karlos had a worn out face but I suspected that he was much younger than he looked. His eyes shone as did his teeth. His weight took all the attention away from his otherwise sharp features. He patted his blond hair in place. The guy looked like he was close to having a stroke due to the run and here he was settling his hair! I have found that men are as vain as women and Karlos was evidence of that.

Uma was staring at me. I did not like her. She had this cunning smile on her face and she kept staring at me. She looked much younger than I, not very tall, about the same height as I, but much leaner. She could pass off as attractive but that look on her face stole the innocence from her age. She looked at me as though I was a threat and I took an instant dislike to her.

Karlos looked pitiful. I looked around for some water for him.

"Why don't you sit down?" I decided to help rather than give in to Uma's bad vibe. But before Karlos could respond, a bell rang in the background and Kurt turned around and walked towards us.

I smiled at Kurt. We meet again, I thought. I wanted to walk up to him, shake his hand and remind him that we had met the previous evening but Kurt looked right through me with no sign of recognition whatsoever. I was now a little mad at him but continued to smile. He just nodded his head and frowned.

Huh? I thought to myself. I met the man last evening. He was the kindest stranger I had ever seen, and here he was pulling an 'arrogant' number on me.

"Sit down," Kurt smiled. His stern demeanor slipped briefly and the smile brought out the kindness in his eyes.

Was it just the three of us? I wondered. Where were the others? We all sat on the wooden stools and the flickering light of the lamps lit up Kurt's face. "And the rest," he pointed behind us, "are going back home!"

We turned around and saw eight people standing about fifteen meters behind us. They were completely drenched. I was confused. Was Kurt on some rescue mission of saving people from the seaway? Was that his way of filling up his seminars?

Veni ran up and placed a stool for Kurt, similar to the one we were sitting on. Kurt now sat down in the centre, facing us.

"My work guarantees results. I am the number one coach in the world," he spoke with arrogance, "not because I charge $25,000 for a workshop or because the President of the United States seeks my guidance. I am the number one coach in the world because I deliver results. I can only deliver results if you follow my instructions. It is clear that I am in charge here. It is clear that you don't know how to take your life in a meaningful direction. It is absolutely clear that you need me to help you. I cannot do that if you don't listen to what I say. I cannot guarantee your success if you don't DO as I say. When you fail to listen to me and do as instructed, I fail to deliver results. I don't fail. Kurt Rinck does not fail. Kurt Rinck delivers." He kicked some sand in the air with his bare foot.

"And those people there," he pointed to the eight people standing like convicts waiting for a verdict, "came to my seminar to seek a change but," he paused and leaned forward as he said slowly, "they cannot follow instructions. They want to change, they have seen the need, but they don't have the humility to make the change within themselves. They think I will give some magic potion which they can make others drink or give them some manipulative formula on how to look people in the eye and make them do what you want them to do. They think that for them to change, others need to change. These people will not get into my seminar."

I wanted to turn around and look at them. One of the men looked familiar but the lights danced and I could not place him. I was curious to see who all were crazy like me to enroll for this seminar to change their life. But for now I continued to look in Kurt's direction. I needed to get my bearings right on what was going on here. "And there were others still who thought today was not convenient for them to embark on the journey to improve their life. They missed to see that change is never convenient. If now is not the right time, it never will be!"

Kurt brushed off some sand from his arm. "You came in here and you were asked to help. Some of you volunteered but others felt that they came here to participate and not to work. And even those who volunteered to help wanted to do it their way. I have no place for people like these in my seminar. They have seen the need to change but I am afraid they are not yet ready to take the leap. They are not ready to serve and they are not ready to be taught. Just because you have the money to get here does not mean I can work on you. Only you can work on yourselves. Life sometimes has to break you some more, pull you down a little bit more, and bring you to the edge of humility where lending a helping hand and allowing yourself to be guided won't be 'below your dignity'. For now, their money will be refunded and they will go back home."

I got it. In an instant I got it. Kurt was testing us right from the registration process on the website. At the reception area, Veni was deliberately asking us to volunteer to see if we would. I had passed the first test. So had Uma and Karlos, I assumed.

Angry conversation had broken out behind us. A man shouted, "You can't send us back like this! I paid the damn money!" With the chaos that had started to build up, I suspected someone might get beaten up. Anyone who paid $25,000 was not going home without a fight, even though their money would be refunded.

And Kurt was unbelievable; he was turning down $200,000 by sending the eight people back. I am sure he could have done 'something' with them. Sure, they were not ready for change because they did not follow instructions, but $200,000 was a lot to refund. Kurt was certainly crazy, and though his ways were severe, his work ethics were worthy of respect.

Kurt however continued speaking to us, turning a deaf ear to the hullaballoo behind, with no hint of worry about the loss of so much revenue. I decided to do the same. I was beginning to understand Kurt's ways and was secretly happy that I had passed the test.

"Your work defines you," Kurt said passionately. "And work is not an eight-hour contract. What you DO every second of your life defines who you will become in the next second. Your acts of kindness, your participation in the contribution towards the lives of others, your intention in lending your support to making other people's lives easier, your eagerness in embracing the world and being an active participant of life is what will make you the person you were meant to be."

"When you isolate your contribution to your own selfish interests, you isolate yourself from success. Success is not about what you make; success is about who you become. And you become a self-centered, stuck-up being if you do not think of others to be worthy of your time and attention. The guys who did not make it were so busy trying to succeed that they became spiritual failures. Success is like making love, you cannot enjoy it alone. Your pleasure necessarily contributes towards another's ecstasy. The self-pleasured person is a lonely per-vert who will not allow another to share of his love."

As Kurt spoke I shuddered at the example. I was not used to discussing sex publicly. I did not even indulge in the 'adult humor' my friends would laugh about. Even though I knew my friends would have other opinions about Kurt's example of success, I got his point.

Kurt was addressing us and I assumed the 'others' had left. Veni appeared with a tray of tea and handed us each a cup. The weather was a little chilly and it was about time for some hospitality. Daybreak seemed hours away. The stars shone brightly on us, competing with the light of the moon. The full moon reflected on the sea and created a straight line of white shimmering light. Every wave that touched the seashore shimmered in that reflection of electric rays as it broke on the sand. I called these 'electric waves'. They had always fascinated me. One moon and so much dance about the moonlight, which it didn't even produce! The sun was mocking the night from the other side of the earth and illuminating it even in its absence. That, according to me, is the highest form of contribution.

"You were asked to wake me up by barking like a dog. In the group of fifteen enrollments only you," he said, pointing to us and looking directly at me, "had the courage to be led. If you cannot follow, you most certainly cannot lead. A leader is also a follower. Even the President of the United States, who virtually is the leader of the world, cannot operate on his whims and fancies. Even though he is a leader, he still has to 'follow' orders and abide by the rules of governance. Poor followers can never make it to the seat of the leader. The people who did not make it had their own creative and 'respectful' ideas on how to wake me up. Their ideas are good for them but that's not how I want to be woken up. When you get up and get to work, you have to deliver results that people can appreciate. You work for yourself but you deliver results for others. Why else would anyone pay you? These guys rang the bell as a more appropriate and effective way of waking me up; little did they realize that the bell was connected to a water bucket that showered them with water for breaking the rule. My point is clear: if you cannot listen to me and follow what I say, then you are wasting my time, which is far more precious than the money you will ever pay me to get your life together."

I understood. Veni had sent everyone who came to the seminar to wake up a 'fictitious' Kurt, to test them. Kurt was here on the beach all the time. There was someone else waiting at the different cottages the people were sent to.

Kurt's ways were amusing in a way and I just could not get over how crazy all of this was. But even though crazy, Kurt made sense. In my profession I have experienced people coming for advice and help and then expecting me to implement the solution as well. They do nothing about it themselves. This leads to a sense of frustration in the advisor, who has not only understood their problem and seen the solution but is doomed to hear about the problem over and over since the advice is never followed. I know the frustration my friends have put me through and I understood what Kurt was getting at. The man was smart and I was beginning to like him. This was what I needed, a no-nonsense coach.

"So I am giving the three of you a chance to withdraw. To take your money and go back to the world you have so carefully made for yourself. This would be your last chance to quit. Moving forward from here there will be no refunds and no questions entertained. If you fail at any step, you will be out of the program, no questions asked. The next seven days there will be only one rule: mine. There will be only one voice: mine. There will be only one leadership: mine. You do not have the right to question, you only follow. So who wants to save their sorry selves and quit?" Kurt thundered.

No one spoke. I had a few questions but for now I would have to keep my attention on finding the answers myself. I hated to be in a situation where I could not ask questions. I always want to know the why, the how, the when, the who, the where of things! I am a very curious being by nature and my curiosity sometimes has gotten me into more trouble than I had bargained for. But right now I had to bury my curiosity and find my own answers.

"So why do you want to change, Priya?" Kurt asked me directly. An electric wave crashed behind him as I gulped my tea. I was not ready for questions. I mean, the man should have asked who I was, where I was from, why I had come here and made some small talk to make me comfortable but here he was questioning me like a cop. And why was I first? Why couldn't he start with Uma? I wanted to protest but I let go.

"Because if I don't change I will lose all that I have built over the years. Because I am fed up and tired of this 'daily' life. I feel stunted. I feel bored. I feel ordinary. I know something big is missing in my life but I don't know what it is. I want more excitement, I want to be richer. I want to be stronger, even more powerful. I want to be free from this nagging feeling that something big is missing from my life. I want to shine and rise to be extra ordinary, to touch that enormity that I sometimes have glimpses of." I was convinced I sounded stupid because Kurt's expression became even sterner.

"And why do you deserve to be rich? Why do you deserve to be extra-ordinary? Why do you deserve any of what you want?" he questioned without hesitation as though he knew my answer already.

Huh? Why do I deserve it? I thought you really didn't deserve to be rich. My neighbor sure didn't deserve all the abundance he had. He was a mean, immoral man and yet he had a dream life; cars, houses, private jet, women, ummm I was not interested in women and those kind he did deserve, but I felt he was quite an undeserving rich man. So why did I need to deserve to be rich and powerful?

"Because I am a good person," I said sheepishly and Kurt roared with laughter. He stood up, held his bulging stomach, and laughed even louder. The waves were getting violent now. They almost reached us, and ebbed just a few feet away. Very soon we would be sitting in water. A seminar in the middle of the sea sounded exciting but right now Kurt was mocking me.

"Since when is goodness equated with riches?" he asked, letting out a faint laugh, almost like a cough.

"Goodness is equated with wealth!" he said as his face changed into a more serious one. "Being good and righteous is true wealth. Pick anyone who changed the world for the better and you will find a good and righteous being behind that movement. Riches can be destroyed and even misused but your goodness is the energy that stays on forever to touch and heal and change generations, long after you have gone. So take a closer look at what you want, for if being rich and powerful is all you seek, join the mafia. Some of the dons are the richest and most powerful people in the world but they can never come out in the open and walk on the beach in freedom. They don't change the world, they destroy it. When you are good and righteous, you are freed from your economic status; it no longer defines or confines you. The economic status is a pre-occupation of the crooked and naïve. And I have no place for either in my seminar."

Cold waves washed over my feet as Kurt's words hit home, leaving behind foamy remnants on my toes as though to cheer me up. Kurt had now turned his attention to Uma. He questioned her on why she wanted to change. I was still ruminating over what Kurt had said to me; I was not interested in what Uma wanted.

I could hear Uma talk, and I even thought I heard a sob, but I was deep in thought about who I was and what I really wanted from my life. Kurt was right. The cars, the houses, the fancy lifestyle did not make me a better person. I was just as confused a person as anyone else. Even though I had a swanky house and a swankier bed I had the same difficulty falling asleep. I had the same nightmares and the same fears. I was economically better but spiritually just as lost.

The water was now ankle-deep and my jeans were wet. I did not have the courage to fold them up because Kurt had not folded his soaked trousers. If he was ok with wet clothes then I figured I should be too. As Kurt finished speaking to Karlos the sky was turning a shade lighter.

"The ocean is a fount of wisdom," Kurt smiled. He turned his stool in the water and faced the ocean. "The ocean is a whole new world. It is as deep as the highest mountain turned down. It hosts life, a life that lives by different rules. We live in an ocean of air and the marine life lives in an ocean of water. The rules of the air do not apply to the rules of the water. When you change dimensions you change form but what remains constant in the whole universe is the form of purpose. The purpose of all life is to survive in the highest order possible. When this purpose is forgotten there is calamity, first in your mind and then in your environment. The ocean, like life, has no favorites, it is impartial. It clearly follows one rule: the survival of the fittest. You are fit when you follow rules, the laws of the universe. Who must teach them to you? Where is the book?" he questioned and looked behind to check if we were listening. "In your heart," he said, tapping his own.

"You," he said pointing towards us, "you have a fragment of the universe in you. A beautiful universe within, and the same one outside. You, by design, are a reflection of the creator. You already are everything you aspire to be. You are everything your eye shows you. You own it. It's your inheritance. Immerse yourself in the abundance the universe offers. Become one with it," he said as he stood up.

"Here is the ocean, go embrace it. Immerse yourself in the wisdom it holds," he said, as he stretched his arms towards the horizon.

The moon had moved towards the horizon and its light gleamed on the dark sea. From where I stood now its reflection seemed like a pathway I could literally walk on. That pathway led to everyone. No matter where I walked on the beach, the path would lead to me. The moon was connected to me personally as it was to everyone else. The universe was connected to me personally as it was to everyone else. I liked this thought and I smiled.

Uma and Karlos ran towards the sea. Kurt looked at me questioningly. What? I almost shivered. What was he expecting us to do? Jump in the sea? Swim in the ocean? Embrace the ocean meant what? Hello! I did not know how to swim! I had been afraid of water all my life. Bathing in the shower and getting wet in the rain was about as much water as I could tolerate. I had never even been in a pool. Was the man suggesting I swim in the sea? Damn! I should have quit when he had said so because now I would have to go back home without a refund.

Uma and Karlos were already in the sea and I could see their heads bobbing in the distance. The waves splashed and broke around me and the water seeped higher into my jeans. "What are you waiting for?" Kurt yelled, turning to look at me.

"I don't know how to swim!" I shouted over the roar of the waves.

"Become a fish," he said, tapping his head as if it was common sense. He broke into a run and I watched his heavy form heave into the water like a dolphin.

Become a fish? That was his answer? Well, it was the wrong answer! I was a girl who did not know how to swim. I was not a fish. This was the deep sea, no it was a deep ocean. As high as the highest mountain downside! I would definitely drown on its inside. I had paid $25,000 for this seminar and instead of teaching me a thing or two about how to change my life around he was telling me to become a fish and jump into the sea. This man was mad, and I was probably madder to join his seminar. I wanted to quit. Damn it!

I walked, no I trudged, into the sea, my footsteps becoming heavier and heavier. $25,000 was too big an amount to lose. If I walked away now I would have nothing. But if I could become a fish this dawn . . . Damn it! How could I become a freaking fish, could someone help me?? A war had broken out in my head. I didn't know whether it was the fear of losing the $25,000 that was killing me or the fear of drowning. I guess if the seminar had cost me $200, I would have picked up my bag and walked out without any regret, but $25,000 was a big amount to forfeit without a fight.

I walked on. Now the water was knee deep. I could see the moonlight still shimmering on the dark sea. The waves were bright and frothy and I could smell and taste the salt already. Something brushed past my foot, maybe a plastic bag pulled from the bottom, and I panicked. My mind had already filled the sea with hungry sharks, man-eating alligators, jellyfish, octopuses, water snakes, not to mention crabs. Every film I had watched about shark attacks now played with new vigor in my head. Every story that I had heard about people drowning, flashed in my mind. I saw images of my swollen body floating towards the shore. I didn't have to make these tragedies mine but I was doing it with all my might. Why were thoughts of the greatest swimmers not crossing my head? Why wasn't I thinking about my niece who won the national swimming championship? Why wasn't I thinking of the lovely dolphins and seahorses, the starfish and turtles, and the magical sea life that I had seen on television? For every shark, there were a million turtles. For every alligator, there were a million seahorses. Nature has evidence of goodness outnumbering the predators and yet the majority lives in terror of the evil few. I decided to be on the side of joy and goodness. To become a fish all I needed to do was; immerse myself in the water, keep my mouth shut, hold my breath tight, move my arms like fins and fan my feet like the tail; and lo! I could swim.

The water had reached my chest and the waves were slapping my face. The salt stung my eyes and I kept spitting out the seawater. I decided to take the plunge. I could see three heads moving up and down in the distance. I had to act fast before time ran out.

I took a deep breath in and let go of the ground beneath my feet. I promptly lost my balance and fell. I tried to catch the water with my hands, but my hands just splashed around. Terrified, I stood up again. I made several attempts at letting go and then landing my feet back on the sand again. It was just not working. I suddenly felt lonely. I wanted to go home. This 'swim like a fish' trick of Kurt's was just not working and I decided to walk back to the shore. 'Try one more time', I told myself sternly. I took another deep breath. This time I heaved into the water like Kurt did and waved my hands consciously but the waves were too powerful for me to make any movement. I was still afloat in the water and the waves pushed me to the shore. It was not so bad, I thought as I got to my feet again. I could see a wave in the distance coming towards me. I had to make it halfway to the wave or else it would push me back to the shore again. So I took a deep breath and plunged into the water, this time headlong. I moved my hands and legs violently pushing at the water. With eyes closed and breath held tight I cut against the bobbing sea and made it a few feet into the deep sea. As I lifted my head and opened my eyes I saw a horrific wave in my face. Before I knew it, it had crashed on top of me pushing me under the water. I panicked and gasped and swallowed water. I took in water through my nose and my mouth opened; I had broken the rule of the water and I was going to be punished. I felt the water tug me in the opposite direction instead of pushing me onto the shore. With water in my lungs and my mouth open, I knew I was going to die. It was dark and before anyone realized I was missing I would be dead. My fear had turned into a reality.

I felt a body near me. A hand grabbed me and pushed me up. My face emerged above the water and I gasped and coughed and almost vomited at the same time. Kurt . . . it was Kurt. He held me tight as he cut through the waves making sure my head was above the water. I had drifted almost ten meters into the sea. It was not much but it was enough to drown a non-swimmer. In less than a minute my feet touched the sand. Kurt still held me while I tried to walk. I was burping and bent over. Kurt lay me down on the sand. "Lie down, turn over," he said, as he turned me over and pressed my back in violent thuds right at the point of my chest. I began to vomit out the water with horrendous sounds. Veni had already clasped a chord around my wrist and I thought she was taking my blood pressure. Kurt had a stethoscope in his hand and as he turned me over he was checking my heartbeat in between my coughs.

I was out in the sea for only a few minutes and a whole first-aid party had come to my rescue.

I was covered in sand and I felt miserable. My lungs hurt, my eyes were stinging, my nose felt raw and my head was ready to burst. The sea did not spare the weak, and it was the same with nature and with life.

"When in the ocean, live by the rules of the ocean. You don't become a fish by living out of human fears," Kurt spoke to me sternly as he widened my eyelids with his fingers and flashed a torch at me.

I could have died. The man could have at least appreciated me for my attempt. It took a lot of courage for me to let go of the ground and act upon his instructions. He was mean and I wanted to go home.

"I don't have the time to pamper you. I have seven days to work on you. So go along and get some rest." He beckoned Veni to look after me.

Uma and Karlos were wading back in the water and even in the dark and through my pain I could sense Uma's delight at my loss. "Is everything ok?" she asked, as she looked at me lying on the sand before someone spoke to her and led her away.

Veni helped me to my feet. "We will watch you for an hour. The ambulance will be here. I hope you will feel better else you will have to be released from the program," she said softly.

"I'm fine," I said, almost pushing her arm off. Actually, I was not fine and I knew I was not going to be fine for the next few hours. I was still coughing and with the sting that I felt in my lungs, I knew they were bleeding. If I was going to be thrown out of the seminar it would not be without a fight!

Veni took me to a villa about five villas away from Kurt's—the fake

Kurt's—villa. It was a beautiful cottage but right now I was in so much pain that I could not appreciate the beauty around me. My clothes were wet and sandy, and my soggy shoes left a watery trail on the wooden floor. A man followed us into the villa with a bag. "These are your clothes and other essentials. I figured you wear size 'small'," Veni said.

"Do you want me to help you change or would you be ok?" Veni asked with concern.

"I'm fine," I almost protested. I took the bag from her and pulled out a black track pant and a black t-shirt. I almost staggered to the bathroom, trying hard to maintain my balance. I looked terrible. My hair was like a mop and my skin was pale. I had no energy left but decided to shower anyway.

What kind of seminar had I gotten myself into? There was no teaching. The man was obviously mean and his ways were certainly severe. It had been crazy the entire time since I had arrived. Eight people were disqualified from being a part of his program because they did not have the humility to help or the ability to follow instructions. Actually, on second thought, those are essential qualities to make a change and a new start. So Kurt was right about that. But was it necessary to throw me into the water? I could have died and what good would that have done to the world or to him or me? It was an unnecessary move. Instead he could have just guided us and given some sort of sermon or tips. Actually, I had heard these sermons before. I had even attended seminars with lots of data and information but the information or stories never changed me. I felt good hearing them but it was not enough to make a connection or to result in change. The seminar was forgotten as quickly as the trainer was. But Kurt was not like that. He was not teaching in the expected conventional manner.

He was allowing me to learn without preaching or sermonizing.

I turned on the shower and stepped into the cubicle. The water was deliciously warm and I began to wash away the sand and the salt that was stinging my skin.

I could not believe I was healing myself with water after I had almost drowned in it. Water is the core element of life on our planet. Life forms have been designed in the same way as the planet. The earth is seventy percent water and so are we. On the outside, we survive in an ocean of air and on the inside, our body lives in a pool of water. We are aware only of the world outside and yet there is untouched wisdom within. Today, to touch that wisdom and make it whole, I had to become a fish. And to become a fish I could not operate from my human ground. I had to let go of what I understand as human and think like a fish. I had to let go of my fears and let go of myself, the self that lives restrained and confined.

Even though Kurt was being his usual self, I was proud that I had attempted to swim. I did swim a few meters and that was commendable. It is true I got caught under a wave but I had let go and ventured to embrace the ocean. I remembered the first seminar I held at twenty-three; my friends and family had felt I was too young to take it on. My uncle, whom I looked up to, advised me to first get a good job and train with someone for a few years to gain enough credibility to launch out on my own as a professional speaker. He felt that I lacked the experience but what he did not know was that I had the courage to swim in the sea. You can swim in the security of a pool but when you get into the sea you are expanding your horizons and casting away limits and boundaries. The sea is the real universe; the pool is a fool's paradise. I began my career at the age of twenty-three, and my uncle was right, people did not take me seriously. I had fallen flat, just as I was thrown to the sea floor by the wave. In that same year my other friends who had opted for the security of the pool seemingly had a great life: a good job, a secure salary, a good boss to mentor, a place to go to work. I, on the other hand, was in the deep sea being tossed by the waves: no income, hearing mindless advice from elders, investing more money in my study, being forced on the shore and constantly facing the obvious threat of drowning and going broke. But every time I fell, I came back and I learnt more. By the end of the year I was the youngest motivational speaker in the country. In one year of falling and floating, I had learnt to swim, and when I did, I left the shore behind and ventured into places my friends could never dream of. Twenty years of security and living under mama's wing makes you a turkey. To be an eagle you have to be thrown off a cliff. When the fledgling is ready to fly, the mother throws it from its nest, which is usually built at the top of the cliff. The baby eagle does not have the privilege of falling off a tree and making attempts to fly; it has to fly, or die.

Kurt Rinck was the eagle and he had taken us to his nest on the cliff and he was going to throw us all off one by one because eagles don't learn how to fly, they were designed to do it.

The shower rejuvenated me. I felt better. My coughing had stopped but my head was aching and so was my chest. It would heal, I told myself as I smiled at my reflection in the mirror. The black tracks and t-shirt fit me perfectly. It had my name printed at the back and I liked that idea. Veni was sitting outside and had me 'under observation'.

"I made some tea, it will make you feel better, try not to eat anything," she smiled.

It was daybreak now and I could see the blue outside. It was 6:32 a.m. The sun would be out any minute, lighting up my world and illuminating the world on the other side through the moon. The sun was on a twenty-four hour job! It worked even when the world turned away from it, without any expectation of compliments and gratitude. Imagine if the sun got upset when people found the moon romantic? Imagine if the sun got mad that the moon took the credit for illuminating the night? Imagine if the sun sulked, and became stubborn and stuck up like me, quitting because there was no acknowledgement! When the sun quits, life ceases to exist on the planet. What we cannot see is the role of the sun that we play in our own small world. When we operate out of acknowledgement and praise and compliments, we are laying the seeds of destruction within and without. To contribute for the sake of contribution is the norm of the universe. Who gets the credit, who gets the glory, is not the agenda. The point is: Did you do what you were meant to do? Did you shine today?

"You can take some rest. I will be here with you until I know you are fine. You will be woken up when it is time to leave," Veni said.

"Leave for where?" I asked now with a sudden spurge of energy. I knew I was not supposed to ask questions but I guess it applied only to Kurt.

"You have a long flight today and I suggest you get some rest, you can't afford to be sick for the next six days!" Veni said as she dialed a number and looked busy on a call.

I had a flight? To where? I thought I would go home after the seminar. Was I going to leave the country? I didn't have anything with me. Someone tell me something! I found myself returning to my frustrated self.

I lay on the bed and I knew I was going to have a hard time 'resting'. Ever since I had signed up for this seminar, which by the way was not a seminar, I had known only one thing—uncertainty. I did not know what to expect. I had no clue what was going on here. Everything that I had ever known about seminars and teaching had been challenged. I had no idea what was going to happen next. This kind of uncertainty could kill someone. Imagine if you were to live your life not knowing what would happen next? Either it would make you 'alive' and 'alert' for real, or it would kill you.

And suddenly, like a flash of lightning, it dawned upon me. This was what I was looking for. This was what was missing in my life. The spirit of adventure, the thrill, the rush, the exploration, the discovery of life. Every day was the same. Tomorrow was as certain as today and today was exactly the same as yesterday. I was living the same life, the same thoughts, the same emotions, day after day, every day. I wanted a change, and change brings uncertainty. Kurt Rinck was uncertainty personified.

Veni was still on the phone. My head was hurting and my eyes felt heavy. When it was time to leave, I would call home and explain. I would find out what was going on when I reached the place. For now I was certain I was safe and I was happy that I was alive. For now I was just grateful that I had grown a little in those few hours. I was amazed that the learning was mine and for real. No one had said anything and yet I had become a bigger person. I knew I was good and there was hope because I had made it into Kurt's seminar. I knew I would fly and conquer the skies and I knew that Kurt would only throw me off the cliff if he believed I could. The world closed in and my body started to repair the damage my naiveté had created. So while my body appeared to sleep on the outside it was working vigorously on the inside ...

I had passed the test.

CHAPTER 4 /

No Identity

I lay half-awake on my bed. I was in a place where I was aware but not done sleeping yet. I could hear Kurt's voice and even in my sleep I could feel his presence near me. Veni was trying to explain to him that I needed medical help. I heard Kurt say as he sat down next to me, "She is a tough one, she won't quit. I don't expect her to. This one is going a long way." I didn't know whether to let him know I was awake or pretend to sleep a little longer. As if by instinct I opened my eyes. Kurt was sitting by my bedside just as I had known he would be. He was wearing the same t-shirt as mine and his breath smelt of coffee.

"Here is a disclaimer form," he said, putting a form on the table as I sat up running my hand through my hair. "If something happens to you, it says that only you are responsible."

Kurt said it so unemotionally. So if I died only I would be responsible. Kurt was right, a voice inside me said. I could not believe I found myself agreeing to his nonsense. The doctor is not a serial killer. He is only trying to set right the problem the patient created in the first place by neglecting or mistreating his body. So how can the doctor be blamed if he failed to set it right? As a result of his irresponsible behavior the patient was going to die anyway. The doctor's intervention at least brought hope into the picture. I was heading for disaster anyway; Kurt was only trying to help, so by reason and logic he should not be held responsible for anything that went wrong from here on.

"Read it and sign it. There are two forms, one for us and one for you." The man was so mean he did not even ask how I was feeling, whether I needed anything, or whether I was hurting. But again, did he need to? Had he not kept Veni to watch over me? She had sat in my room the entire time that I was sleeping. I'm sure she must have had better things to do but she was serving me, which was probably outside her job profile. Did that not reflect Kurt's concern? But no! I wanted to hear it in so many words. I wanted his affection and attention in a way that I understood it. That is how I have broken my heart all my life. I had missed the love and concern that people showed me in their actions. I concluded that he did not love me because he did not say the words that I wanted to hear. But today Kurt's actions conveyed something to me. Oh man. I was not the same person that I had been yesterday. These were not ordinary thoughts. I was in a 'supposed' seminar and I was my own teacher. Kurt's presence was just incidental. I suddenly began to love this game.

"This," he said, holding out a file, "contains your license to live."

"License to Live!" I said out aloud.

"You are on a learner's license for the duration of the seminar and if you pass the test and learn well, you will be granted your license to live. This says that you are not only a safe driver of your life, but that the people who will accompany you in your journey will also be kept safe."

I was totally baffled. Kurt was going to give me a license to live. Just like a license to drive a car, he was going to give me a license for my own life. This was turning out to be a fun game and I was excited.

"Here is your course material," he said waving another file, a beautiful, black leather-bound file. It had the words "My License To Live" embossed in gold on it. "This file needs to be filled every day before you end your day. The file will be turned in after seven days and a final evaluation will be done. Whether you pass or fail will be decided on the basis of this file," he said, putting the file on the table.

"Two hours from now you will leave for the airport. Veni will accompany all of you. Your passport and ticket will be at the airport. Your instructions will reach you when it is time for you to have them. Have a safe flight. Hope to see you after seven days," Kurt said, getting up. The kindness in his blue eyes had emerged again. He took my hand in his, just as he had done on the seaway the previous evening, and said, "You are a tough one. You will go a long way. And my seeing that is not enough; your knowing it for yourself is what will make the difference."

Before I could say anything—not that I knew what to say or how to react—Kurt turned around and left the room with Veni in tow.

I puzzled over Kurt's words. He had enrolled me in a seminar and now he said 'meet you after seven days?' This was crazy. What did he want us to do for seven days without him? Who would teach us? Who would guide us? And what exactly did he charge us the $25,000 for? Where was I going? I had almost drowned and died, for heaven's sake! Now even if I wanted to argue or fight, I did not have the energy.

I sat up, surprised that I felt better. I guess my brains were working and my body felt alive with the suspense about what was going to happen next. It was almost as if I had bought a ticket to a very expensive thriller movie. The only difference was that this was reality and not fantasy. And like in a movie, I did not know the script. I would discover what was to happen next only when I moved to the next level.

I picked up the disclaimer form from underneath the black file. It was a regular disclaimer form. Just like forms I sometimes used for my own seminars. Sometimes people behave irresponsibly and sometimes things go wrong, so it's always better to have the legalities covered.

The disclaimer read:

> There is only one real cause and that is me. Negatively or positively, it is I who create the effect in my environment. And it is true that everything that happens in my world and my environment and my life and my heart can be traced down to the way I think and the choices I make and the work I do. There is no other and nothing else that is responsible for who I am and what I do. It all starts and ends with me. It is only when I take responsibility for the state of my world; I stand a chance to change my life.

Signed: Priya Kumar
10th January 2005

Now how can you argue with this? First of all, there was no one to argue with. The man who wrote the paper was no longer there. I did not have permission to ask questions, let alone argue. If I asked, I could be accused of not following instructions. I had no option but to agree. Actually, as much as my ego was playing the 'defensive' game,

I did agree with every word that was written in the disclaimer. The life that I was living was my doing and only if I recognized it as my doing would I be able to change it around. I took the pen and scribbled my name.

My phone beeped. It was my mother. I knew there would be a whole string of complaints and I took a deep breath before answering. Sometimes, dealing with your own mother is like swimming in the deep sea; it is a battle of your own imaginary sharks with hers.

Explaining my seven-day workshop to mom was easier than I thought it would be. After all, she had always supported me. And though the words she said did not sound good, her actions were always in sync with love. As I began to understand Kurt, I began to understand my mother as well.

Veni came into the room. "We will leave in one hour. Your bags are already at the airport. I will see you in the lobby." Before I could react she had disappeared.

Now where did my bags come from? I had not brought any! I held my head in my hands and wanted to pull out my hair in frustration.

Surrender, I told myself. Let go of your insane habit of wanting to know everything before you do anything! There was a bigger intelligence at work here. Surrender and learn. The future does not have to be frightening. Today was yesterday's future and tomorrow will be today's future. The future is created one day at a time. If today is committed to growth and learning, and if I promise to live tomorrow with the same commitment and carry on that promise for the rest of my life, then my future is sorted out. There was nothing to fear except my own choices for today.

I got up and washed my face. I looked better. There was a pair of black sports shoes, my size, next to the bed. Mine were still wet and now rather shrivelled. I decided to leave them. Veni could send them home along with my clothes.

I walked out, ready, with the files in my hand. The breeze flipped the pages of the file and I began reading the first page. It had a small license that said: Learning to Live—valid for seven days. It had one of my favorite pictures, obviously downloaded from my website.

I paused and signed my name on my learner's license to live. I smiled. This really seemed like a game.

I was going to learn to live. At the age of thirty, I was going to learn to live. So until now I had been reckless? Sort of like a reckless driver? A danger to myself and others? Well, to be totally honest, I was an unlicensed driver, maybe not dangerous but certainly ignorant and naïve, and in some countries that *is* termed dangerous.

I stopped to stare at the horizon and wondered where Kurt was taking us. Even through the thrill of it all, I could not help hoping that I was booked in business class. My License To Live was tucked under my arm. This was my course material. I decided to read it on the plane so I could prepare myself in advance for the next seven days. I always liked to be ahead and sometimes I was so focused on getting ahead that I didn't realize that I was running in the wrong direction. Once you have gone astray though, the way back home is a very painful journey. I had spent a great deal of time on this constant return journey especially when it came to the men I fell in love with!

I walked up to the lobby. Veni was nowhere in sight. A small bus was standing at the entrance and I wondered if this was for us.

I looked at the watch; it was ten minutes to six. I saw Veni walking towards me in a hurry. Karlos was at her heels but Uma was nowhere in sight. "That's the bus," Veni pointed at the minibus I had seen.

"But we still have ten minutes," I said, quite surprised.

"If you are on time, you are late," she said, as she and Karlos hopped onto the bus.

"But where is Uma?" I asked, surprised and concerned. "If she does not show up in two minutes, she is late," Veni said, taking a window seat.

I sat on the seat behind Veni and started my stopwatch, before I could lift my head I saw Uma running for the bus. Much to my dismay she made it twenty seconds in time.

As the bus started, Veni stood up. "I need to check your purse," she said to me.

Frisk my purse? Was I going to carry weapons and explosives in my purse? The hotel had not bothered with it and there was security at the airport; why did she need to check my purse?

I had a hundred questions in my head but silently handed the purse over. Veni pulled out my wallet and opened it while I watched. She placed it on the empty seat next to her. She took out the notes and loose change as well. She took out my mobile phone, driver's license, and my identity card. She gathered them and put them in a plastic zip lock bag. She repeated the process with Uma and Karlos.

"This will be kept in my custody until you return," she said nonchalantly and began to stash away our items in a safe-like suitcase.

I wanted to protest but didn't want to be the only one, since Uma and Karlos said nothing. Now we were three strangers on an insane journey with no identity, no money, and no access to the world. We were going to fly off to a strange land with nothing on us except two files under our arm. And we had paid $25,000 to be broke and stripped of our very identity.

I needed to occupy my mind intelligently before I strangled Veni and the bus driver and ran home. I opened the black leather file: My License To Live. I hoped that maybe a few lessons would help in understanding what I was supposed to understand and feel at that moment. I took a deep breath and flipped open the first page, it was blank. I turned the next page, it was blank too, and as I frantically flipped through the other pages I found that they all were blank.

"You have to fill this every day," Veni helped.

I shut it and sighed painfully. I had paid $25,000 and signed away my life. I had given up every bit of security I owned including my access to the world that I knew. I was going off to 'nowhere' literally and I was expected to be sane. If you want to change your life, burn your bridges back to your familiar world. The Trojans did the same thing with their army. When the troops landed in a country they burnt their ships. So the only way home was to win. And the price to pay for losing was death. There was no escape. Because winners don't escape, they win or they die trying.

I turned around and looked at Uma. She looked pretty calm, staring out of the window. Karlos looked quite composed too. I wondered if they were as freaked out as I was for I guess from the exterior I looked fine too. Somehow we all seem to excel at pretence. Pretending our way through life. If we suppress the pain, ignore our mistakes, and turn a blind eye to the wrongs for long enough, everything will be ok. But life cannot be lived in ignorance, pretence, or suppression. Life is lived in confrontation and acknowledgement. The next six days would prove to be the greatest lessons I would ever have learnt in my life.

CHAPTER 5 /

The Jump

We arrived at the airport in silence. I had never communicated with Karlos or Uma, except for the occasional Hello, Hi, or How are you? All of us had been so extremely challenged and stressed that no one initiated any small talk. I am normally the first to start a conversation and take the initiative to get to know people but right now we were all in our shells, thinking, evaluating, reflecting, and scheming. The bus halted at the international airport. The driver took out three black bags that were identical except for the different color tags on them. The black tag read 'Karlos', the pink tag read 'Uma', and the yellow tag was mine.

Veni handed us our passports and a pouch containing the tickets. Before I could reach out and take the pouch from her, Veni withdrew her hand and held out another pouch.

"This has a mobile phone," she said very sternly. "Between the three of you, you are entitled to only one phone call in the next two days. After you make the phone call, the line will disconnect." She handed me the phone pouch. She had made the right choice in selecting me to be in charge of it, I thought.

"Be careful in the choices you make. You have two days to complete your task. The instructions will be given to you on the flight. Remember that you have no money and no access to the world except this phone. No matter what you do, stick together and follow the instructions." Veni looked extremely serious as though we were going on a dangerous mission. Actually, on second thoughts, we *were* going on a dangerous mission. Now if only she would hand me the tickets pouch it would bring my raging curiosity to rest. I knew people in most countries and I wanted to know where we were going.

"Jack," she pointed to the driver, "will escort you from here. Here are your tickets. Good Luck!" Veni said, as she handed us our pouches.

I flung open the pouch and almost tore the ticket. Malaysia was to be our destination. I frowned. Damn! I did not know anyone in Malaysia. There went my plan of getting some help . . . I flipped through the passport and there was a Malaysian Visa. Kurt must be well connected in the embassy to pull this through, I thought.

Jack had already started walking towards the VIP entrance and we all had to hasten to keep pace with him. I could see Karlos panting already. I wondered what he wanted to achieve out of the seminar and decided to chat with him on the flight.

Jack led us through the security to the special check in counter. The airhostess was delighted to see us. We got VIP treatment all the way. Kurt had booked us in Business Class after all. You would not expect anything less for $25,000.

Jack obviously wielded a lot of influence at the airport. We walked past all the gates and found a Mercedes-Benz waiting to take us to the aircraft. Oh my God! We would be going in a car. I felt like a rock star heading for a concert; wearing an outfit with my name, escorts all the way, a swanky car to take me to the aircraft. This was amazing. In the car, Uma and Karlos got talking. Apparently, it was Uma's dad who had wanted her to join the program and obviously he had sponsored it. Karlos was a multi-millionaire from New York. He had everything and yet everything was missing from his life. At forty-five he was single and had few friends. He was the perfect example of 'its lonely at the top'. Every time I tried to enter into the conversation both of them would keep quiet as though my company was unwelcome. I am a 'people' person and starting a conversation and making friends is part of who I am, but Uma and Karlos were keeping me out. Maybe they had a chance to hook up while I was sick all day. I didn't know what inhibited them from making friends with me and I decided to lie low for a while. Maybe I could try a different approach during the flight.

The car came to a halt at a private Jet. It was a Learjet 45. That's a neat private jet for those who are not familiar with private jets. My jaw dropped to the ground. Kurt was sending us to Malaysia in a private jet! I had not expected this! I had always wanted to travel in a jet plane. Heck no, I had always wanted to own one! And here I was, my dream come true. Uma looked towards me and smiled saying, "I cannot believe this." She looked like an excited schoolgirl, and I tried to hide my own childish delight.

We were welcomed with a hospitality that I had never experienced. It was a swanky jet, or maybe all private jets are swanky. The seats were cream-colored leather. The interior was plush; there was a mini bar, and a straight view into the cockpit. There were only window seats, two seats per row with a large table jutting out at every seat. The seats were not seats, they were literally sofas. I was excited. I ran up to the seat just behind the cockpit. This was a dream come true. The hostess brought some champagne. See, I don't drink alcohol but this was not the time to fuss. When in a jet plane, do what all jet-setters do. Toast and drink!!!

We still had a few minutes before takeoff and I asked the hostess if I could visit the cockpit while in flight. She was polite enough to tell me that I could ride with the pilot if I wanted. I had always wanted to sit in a cockpit. This was turning out to be a cool seminar after all! I could not understand why Kurt had been scaring us and testing us so much. This was quite unlike Kurt's behavior, to load us up in a private jet. It's like when you expect the worst, the skies clear up and the sun shines on you; and when you expect the sun to shine, torrential rain drowns you. Kurt, like life, was so unpredictable. Or was he? I think Kurt, like life, was full of surprises and full of fun. Only when there is change, there is a chance to grow. The universe is designed to follow that. When the seasons change, we need to change the way we live our lives. If there was no change and we lived in the same predictable environment, we would stagnate both physically and spiritually. Change brings life and it brings growth. Just a few hours ago I had almost drowned and I was sick enough to be in hospital, but because there had been so much anticipation and hype about the future, I was alive. I was alive and kicking. I feel sickness is a sign of stagnation and I had stagnated my approach towards life a long time ago.

The hostess soon got our attention. "Before we take off for Malaysia I would like to give you your instructions," she said. I had expected a younger and sexier hostess but Linda was in her forties and had been flying private jets for nineteen years. As she spoke, the captain entered. He was also in his late forties. An Asian man who spoke with a typical Asian accent. I suspected it was Malaysian. He messed up genders and his English was not fluent. However, he was courteous and confident, the qualities one seeks in a pilot. Linda handed us each an identical brown packet. I placed my file on the table and tore open my packet. It contained another file labeled INSTRUCTIONS and read:

Priya,

(There was no dear Priya or dearest Priya. Just by the mode of address you could see Kurt Rinck at work.)

You are headed for Genting Highlands, Malaysia. In Genting Highlands you will meet Bomo, the man who keeps the future. Take your message from him and get to the Malaysian International Airport. Your flight leaves at 11 p.m. on 12th January. Your passport and ticket will be given to you at the airport. If you don't make it to the flight, you have failed. If you don't take the message from Bomo, the man who keeps the future, you have failed.

Fill your **My License to Live** file everyday. That is your final evaluation.

You are entitled to one phone call during your stay in Malaysia. One phone call between three people. You will have no money and no identity. Make your choices wisely.

Stay together.

Love and Prayers,

~ Kurt Rinck

Love and prayers my foot! The excitement of being in a jet plane had evaporated while reading the instructions and now I had turned around and was looking at Uma and Karlos whose expression mirrored my own.

I had just dealt with the fright of having my money, phone, and identity taken away by Veni on the bus. One look at the jet plane and I had forgotten all about it. Now with Kurt's instructions, my fear had returned! First of all, I did not like the idea of having no identity. Jack had accompanied us and handed our passports to Linda before we got into the jet. We could have at least been entrusted with our own passports. To be in a foreign country with no identity is like playing with fire. One could be arrested, or die, or face terrible things. And no money? How in the world does one survive without money? And just one phone call between three people? How do we decide whose phone call is important? This was crazy! Uma and Karlos were clearly not particularly fond of me. And Uma was already eyeing the phone. What about food? Where would we live? How would we travel? Wait a minute! Who was Bomo? Where did he live? Where was I to find him? And how can anyone keep the future? The future hasn't even occurred so how can anyone keep it? This was a ridiculous assignment! Could someone tell me what was going on?

The co-pilot came in and introduced himself but for the first time I was not interested. Linda gave the safety instructions and the plane was soon speeding on the runway.

Once we were airborne I turned and asked Karlos, "What are we going to do?" He seemed like my only hope! Maybe because he was the eldest of the three, I assumed he would know something. After all he had lived twenty odd years more than me . . . But Karlos' answer shattered my hopes. "I don't know," he said with fear in his eyes.

"What are we going to do?" Uma chipped in and looked at Karlos and me for an answer. She was obviously the youngest and was thinking like me.

"We will figure a way," I said, taking control. Someone had to take control here and since there seemed no volunteers, I stepped in.

"Let's take it one step at a time. One minute at a time, one hour at a time," I spoke almost like the corporate guru I had been for so long. This was no time for a motivational talk, I reprimanded myself. But I guess some words of confidence and courage do help in clearing the negative emotions in a stressful situation.

"So what should we do?" Uma asked partly curious, partly confrontational.

"Well, for now, lets enjoy the jet ride, eat some good food, and . . ." I lowered my voice, "lets pack some food and build a reserve. Order your hearts fill and then let's pack it and bag it. So at least the food is sorted for two days." I saw Uma's face light up.

See, I was much smarter than I gave myself credit for. There was always a solution. There was always a way out, if we didn't focus on the problem. Everything can be solved one tiny piece at a time. Even a jigsaw puzzle is built one piece at a time. You can't put all the pieces together all at once. You pick one strand and then build upon it.

"Can I have three beers?" I heard Karlos' voice behind me. The man was going to stock beers and not food! I almost burst out laughing.

I wanted to use the flying time to get to know Uma and Karlos and instead here I was getting to know myself better. I had to think fast and I had to think straight. Who was Uma? Why was she here? What did Karlos want to achieve with this seminar? It all seemed irrelevant. How were we to survive? How were we to get to Bomo without any money? How were we to lie low and not be caught by the police? All these seemed necessary plans!

"Stock the food." I again looked at Uma and Karlos. "Eat your fill and try to rest. It looks like we will need the energy for the next two days." I sounded like the captain of a lost ship.

"I'm scared," Uma said, looking at me with puppy dog eyes.

"I'm scared too," I caught myself saying. "But we will handle whatever comes, together." I smiled.

Sometimes we are so afraid to admit to our own fears that the mere pretence of bravery shatters us. It's ok to confess that you are afraid as long as you are willing to move on despite your fears. Because we all admitted we were afraid, we knew we had to support each other. If I had pretended to be the brave one Uma would have certainly clung on to me and brought us both down.

"Nothing is going to happen, everything has been designed for a purpose. There is a teaching in every event and there is a learning we are here for. One thing is certain, the only way to safety and victory is to follow instructions," Karlos spoke with a deep wisdom. So the man was not a stupid, rich man after all. He was smart and he was wise. I wondered what was missing in his life for him to surrender himself to Kurt to change it. I guessed in time I would find out; at that point I had a job to do.

Linda kept a straight face while we continued to order food for over an hour, until I guess we had exhausted the supplies of the aircraft.

I had enough stock of food to last me two days and I was hoping that Uma and Karlos had taken responsibility for their own. I turned around and smiled at them and they smiled back. Crisis brings people together, especially when everyone is equally at risk. Nations come together during wars, the world comes together during natural calamities. Just a few moments ago when there was peace, Uma and Karlos were indifferent, and now that we were facing a challenge, we became a team.

Uma tapped my shoulder with the black file. "We need to fill this every day. Do it before you sleep so that it will be one task done." She smiled and turned to Karlos to tell him the same.

I groaned. I was tired. I had almost drowned and been sick enough to be in a hospital . . . Oh no! I had started on my old routine again. I could not believe I was going to use my drowning and being sick as an excuse to flee from my current responsibility. That's what the beggars do on the streets of India. They show you their self-inflicted wounds and tug at your emotions to get money. I felt like a beggar myself. I decided to let go of the 'I nearly drowned and was nearly sent to the hospital episode' and decided never to bring it up again. I was here in a private jet! What about that? But you have no money and no identity, the cynical me spoke up! With this debate in my head about what I had and what I didn't have, I knew I was going to be a loser once again because what I didn't have always seemed more than what I had.

I opened the black file and took out a pen. "You must write every day," Kurt had said. I groaned as I scribbled:

"I will write tomorrow." I smiled cleverly and shut the file. Kurt had written write 'something' and I was happy. He had found his match. I shut my eyes and prepared to rest.

See, I had missed one of the most important lessons in life. We always lead ourselves to believe that we can outsmart others. So in writing 'I will write tomorrow', I was trying to act smart by beating the system, by beating Kurt. But when I beat Kurt I was the loser. I was supposed to write what I learnt today and I was too tired to evaluate my day, an extra ordinary day. I had been too tired for many years to think about my life, to question my contribution, to keep a tab on my growth. When it came to taking an account of my life, I was too tired to write, too tired to think, and too tired to act. Because I had no account of my life, I spent my energy in repeating every yesterday. I could never change it because I was too tired to even see that I was failing.

Uma and Karlos had been better because they had filled pages with what they had learnt. I, however, was conserving my energy. After all, I had almost drowned . . . Oh shut up! I told myself before I took the beggar attitude any further.

I began to tilt my seat and felt Uma's hand on my shoulder, "You have not written yet! Follow instructions!" she spoke with authority. I wanted to bop her head and tell her to mind her own business but I decided to fill the damn journal instead.

I am tired. I have started out on an assignment that I had no clue about. It's almost as though I have been conned into being here. I enrolled for a seminar and this seems more of a life-threatening adventure than a seminar.

I made a lot of assumptions when I enrolled and now I am facing a reality that I was not prepared for. I cannot even count how many times my assumptions have landed me in a similar position.

I have never swum in my life, mainly because I was afraid of the water. And because I was afraid, I was convinced I would drown. But today I almost swam and I did not drown. I was not learning how to swim, I was learning to face my fears, for once I can face my fears, I can learn how to swim.

My past seven years have been about praise and admiration. I did not realize it but I had begun to depend upon it. When Kurt did not praise me for being brave enough to attempt to swim, I felt purposeless. I was almost living my life for what others would say and what others would feel, than for my own evolution. I was doomed to misery..

I feel at a total loss. I am nobody and I don't even exist for the duration of two days. I don't exist as the person I have known so well: Priya Kumar, the corporate guru. I don't like being without an identity. Who am I if I don't have a title defining me? Am I more than my title? Am I about to be re-introduced to myself? What if someone asks me, "Who are you?" What will I say? Who am I? I am a lost kid on the block pretending to be brave, I guess. Now that's what my title hides, and maybe that's why I need to let go of it to find the little lost girl and tell her to grow up. How else will I ever find myself?

I don't like being without money! Money has been my greatest security and greatest aspiration. I always have more money in my purse than I need . . . for . . . just in case. And because I always had more, I treated money carelessly. Actually I treated money carelessly even when I had less of it. To be honest I have never had respect for money. And so I have never respected anything that money bought. My possessions are as unkempt as my bank accounts. If it weren't for my mother, I would long be broke. And now I have no money whatsoever, and I realize how important money is as an exchange for survival! How would I survive without money? And who would I become if I learnt to survive without money? Is it possible that if money no longer defines me, I will be richer no matter what my economic status?

I don't know whom I am supposed to meet. How can I find one man in a big country when all I have is his name and what he does? How can I locate someone without any direction or detail? How will I make it all happen in two days? And what if I do attempt to find him, and what if I do find Bomo? Does that mean that I can find anything I am looking for? Does it mean that life also comes with a hazy hint of where I am supposed to head, and how I get there is a process where I discover myself and grow as a person and spirit? Does it mean that in finding Bomo I can find anything that I need?

How can anyone keep the future? The future is not even here. What kind of man is Bomo who keeps the future? Whose future? I have so many questions and I don't like that I cannot reach out to someone and ask for answers! Is it that I am answering my questions by moving forward on the task? And who has the answers really? When I felt lost, who could give me any answers? When the question is mine, then the answer should also be mine. Is it then true that I am the answer to my question?

And how in the world do I KNOW so much? No one is teaching me here. There are no tips, no guidance, nothing. Then where is this knowing coming from? The more I reflect the more I KNOW.

I love this seminar after all.

I already felt good. I felt wise. I felt kind of free. I looked around before I admitted to myself that I actually felt happy writing the journal.

I tilted my seat and closed my eyes. I had earned my rest after all. I must have slept long because when Linda tapped my shoulder for the umpteenth time and I woke up bleary-eyed, Uma was giggling out loud. "Are we landing?" I asked getting up and straightening my seat.

"No, but I have instructions for you," Linda spoke with a smile.

I looked at the watch. It was 4 a.m. Malaysian time. I checked my purse—it was still bloated with the food. I wondered if I could ask Linda for some money. Would that be kind of shameful? Maybe I could ask for a loan and wire her the money when I got home. In Malaysia, even a couple of hundred dollars can let you survive for two days. I have never asked anyone for money in my whole life. I guess, somehow, I have associated asking with begging. So even at times when I have really needed help, I have always been hesitant to ask. And because I never asked, I never got it. I somehow expected people around me to understand me and help me without saying a word. That's quite a high expectation, one that only leads to disappointment. My frequent disappointments had hardened me so much that I had isolated myself from all the help that I could have got. Here I was breaking some of my rules. For all I cared I could starve, I was not afraid of that. Being in jail in a country like Malaysia was a thought compelling enough for me to beg. "Linda," I said, looking around to get Uma and Karlos' support. But Linda had her own agenda.

"In fifteen minutes from now you will be dropped at Genting Highlands. The sky is clear and the sun will be up in a couple of hours. You have your instructions on what to do there. Here is your gear, please wear it as instructed," Linda said, as she handed us haversacks with a lot of hooks and fasteners.

Why would I wear this gear, I thought? It looked like mountaineering gear. Maybe I could stuff the food in the haversack, I thought, and looked around for the zipper.

"What are you doing?" Linda almost screamed.

"I'm looking for the zip. I want to put my purse in the bag." I was startled at her scream and the haversack almost fell from my hand.

"This is not a haversack," Linda slapped her head. "It's a parachute!"

Now this was the time I could have had a heart attack. "Parachute for what?" I almost screamed as Uma started to laugh behind me.

"Why the hell are you laughing?" I barked at Uma who continued to laugh despite my outburst. I had panicked and I needed to urgently kill someone to show Kurt how seriously I had panicked.

I have never understood why people suddenly start laughing in the face of extreme fear just as people start to cry in times of extreme joy. I knew Uma was not laughing at me but she was laughing at the gravity of the situation and my reaction to it. She was laughing because she saw herself in me, and I looked terrible. My hair was a mess, the salt from the sea had made it hard and gritty. My voice was croaking, my eyes were red and my purse was filled with loot. On hindsight, I could laugh at myself too. But right then, I wanted to kill someone, even if it was Uma.

"Are you crazy?" I protested. Why wasn't Karlos saying anything? He was the man after all. He should have been standing up for all of us.

Instead of beating up this crazy woman he was harnessing his chute. I don't know how but I always land up with the wrong men, even if it is a grown-up rich man in a jet plane. Why couldn't he support my anger? I stood there fuming and shaking with terror. Karlos had already strapped himself on. No questions asked. Coward, I scoffed in my head.

Uma was blank. She was staring and waiting for acknowledgement. "What are you staring at? Wear the damn gear!" I shouted as I fumbled to look at mine.

"How do you wear this freaking thing?" my voice shook with anger as I barked at Linda.

"The instructions are on the paper here, ma'am!" she said, politely ignoring my violent eruption.

There I was doing it again. I was directing my anger in the wrong direction. I was mad at Kurt. I was terrified at my own inability to cope with the current situation and I was giving Linda, Uma and Karlos a hard time. They were not responsible for my stress, yet they were the victims of my fears. After all this fuming and fretting, when some calm prevailed, I could see my stupidity and I didn't know how to apologize. Normally I would have left it unaddressed assuming they would understand, which they normally never did.

"I'm sorry," I spoke sheepishly. I looked at Uma who was all strapped and hooked.

"Can you help me with this?" I asked her. Uma came over and helped me get plugged and hooked.

Large glasses that looked like ski glasses were on the table.

"So you expect us to just jump off?" I asked Linda, my voice laced with sarcasm.

"We will clear the cabin and close the cockpit doors. All your belongings will be stashed away. You have a compartment on your chute in which you can stash three kilos of your stuff," she said, pointing to my purse which was filled with stolen food. "You will jump out one by one," she continued decisively.

"Have any of you used a parachute before?" Linda asked. All of us seemed to have lost our voices and could only shake our heads in disbelief.

"Well, there is a ball on the edge of the sack," she said, pointing to the ball on the sack. "When you jump, try and keep your arms open sideways and your legs curled backwards. You will be jumping from an altitude of 15,000 feet. You will drop at the speed of about 115 kilometers per hour. When you are at approximately 5,500 feet you will pull this ball and your parachute will open. Your landing time will be approximately 5 minutes. You will hopefully touchdown at a radius of half a kilometer from each other."

As Linda spoke, I took mental notes. There was no point in writing this down, because I didn't think it would be wise to open up a sheet of paper while falling from the sky to figure out what to do next.

I tried to picture the entire fall in my mind's eye. I could visualize Uma falling, I could certainly visualize Karlos falling, but I could not, for the love of God, visualize myself falling. Why could Kurt not have just dropped us off at Genting? Err.... Technically he was 'dropping us off' but what I meant was, why couldn't he 'land' us !!!! He rented this whole fancy aircraft only to dump us from the sky? And what if the parachute did not open? What if I panicked and forgot to open my parachute? Actually the truth is I *had* panicked. The beauty about panic is that after it strikes, you don't understand any instructions. "I don't know anything," I said out aloud as tears began to build up.

"And so it's the time to learn," Karlos said as he took my hand.

I'm afraid of heights. I am afraid of anything there is to be afraid of. It's simple: if someone is afraid of it, then maybe I can try being afraid too. But now I had to get on the other side of the equation and try my hand at being brave.

I would only figure out later that we could not have done the jump during the day because that would have brought attention to us. We had to do it while it was dark. What I did not know is that a night jump is a hundred times more dangerous than a day jump. What I did not know is that you needed a license to do a solo jump. What I also did not know is that a first-timer never does a solo jump. I was glad that I did not know all this; knowledge sometimes can kill you, especially if that knowledge contains facts about your very survival. Knowledge has two ends. One end of knowledge limits you, while the other liberates you. I was accidently on the edge of liberation, literally.

"You have 5 minutes," Linda announced, adjusting her watch. Karlos got busy stuffing the food in the small jacket of the chute bag. I began to stuff mine too. Besides the food there was nothing in the purse that would help us survive anyway.

"Your belongings and your bags will be at the airport when you arrive tomorrow," Linda smiled.

"Follow the instructions," Karlos said to Uma and me, both of us looking half-dead from fright. "Follow the instructions and you will live."

I looked out of the window. The sky was lit with stars and the moon was faithfully by their side. Below were the dense Genting forest highlands. Where would we land? In the forest? I was certainly going to die. Kurt could have just killed the pilot and asked us to fly the aircraft. That would have been easier. I was losing my mind and my mindless alternate solutions were a clear proof of that.

Linda had cleared the cabin while I waged a mental war. Uma squeezed herself in my chair to seek comfort in this time of crisis and I wanted to squeeze into Karlos'. What had we bought ourselves into? Who knew whether this would be the last time we would see each other? Who knew what would happen next?

"Wear your glasses and your watch. Keep tab of the altitude," Linda said, tapping the large dial watch that showed the altitude.

The alto meter watch was a gigantic watch. You could see the fluorescent needles and the numbers clearly even in the dark. I had to check for 5,500 feet and then tug at the ball on the right of the bag with my right hand.

Linda took us to the side of the door. The cockpit panel was shut and Linda was also wearing gear. Was she going to jump with us? That was some relief. My hopes were soon shattered as I caught a glimpse of a rope that securely attached her to the leg of the seat. Linda was not jumping off, she was just going to make sure that we did . . . without her. With the ideas that were erupting in my head, I would have taken Linda down with us, with or without the parachute.

Linda told us to hold on tightly to the metal rung next to the door. "Who goes first?" she asked. Karlos volunteered.

"I will go next," Uma spoke. She did not want to be last.

"I will go after the captain," I said but no one saw the humor in my idea. Linda ignored my comment totally as she heaved open the door. A gush of wind like a heavy wave of water entered the cabin. The plane shook a bit and we could have all fallen out. The wind was on an evacuation mission because it kept tugging and pulling at us as it did a whirlwind number inside the aircraft. I held on tight to the metal strip and I was not letting go. A tissue paper flew around and landed on Uma's face. I let go of one hand to remove the paper which now flew around violently and stuck to the ceiling.

We had lost a lot of altitude and my stomach felt really queasy. I should not have overeaten. I began to regret all the food I had so greedily stuffed into myself.

"Go." I could see Linda's face as she pushed Karlos out of the aircraft. I tried to look through the window and I saw a speck falling into the night sky with the silver star on the black parachute bag now gleaming bright in the moon light. Karlos looked like a shooting star heading for the forest.

My heart raced as I let go of Uma's hand.

Keep an eye on the watch. At 5,500 feet tug the ball on the right. And you will be ok. If I had to die, I would die like a hero. Heck, I was not being a hero, I was committing suicide! I was going to leap off an aircraft and then fight for my life! Kurt Rinck was insane, I cursed at the sky!

I shivered violently as Uma disappeared. It was freaking cold and my hands had frozen tight on the metal strip. There was no way to let go of my grip, or so I wished.

Uma had shot off like a star without as much as a yelp and now the drama queen was next. I was the noisiest person my family had known. I created the greatest fuss and made the loudest ruckus. I would do crazy things according to my fancy and I would do them loud. I don't know if the drama was to camouflage my own fear or to convert the fierce energy of terror into fun. But no matter what my intention was, the more I stood on the tight rope and created a scene, funny or intense, my fear only grew. With my habit of making a scene, I knew I was not going down without one tonight.

I opened my mouth to say my usual, "I can't do this, I will die. Can you jump with me?" But Linda beat me to it. "Keep your arms open and legs curled. Pull the ball when you reach 5,500 feet. God bless you." And she yanked my arm and pulled me loose towards her.

The wind was fierce, it was messing with my breathing. I could see the skin on Linda's face fluttering as the wind forced itself on her as she opened her mouth to speak. I was standing on the edge of the floor and a dark endless pit stood waiting for me. Linda was holding my arm cleverly so that I could not get a grip of hers. I looked down and began pleading with Linda. "I can't do this, I will die . . ." But before I could move a step away, I felt her hand on my back and a push as I fell headlong into the dark abyss.

I had had nightmares of falling: falling off a cliff, falling of a building and even falling off a staircase. But the experience of falling out of the sky beat any of those nightmares. I knew that this experience would haunt me for the rest of my life.

My soul had long past left my body as I fell headlong. I opened my mouth to scream but there was no sound. Instead I swallowed a gallon of air which I would spend the whole day releasing. I somersaulted violently because sometimes I saw the stars and moon and sometimes pitch darkness. My arms were flung open and threatened to break loose from my shoulder sockets, my legs were curled backwards, and my back arched painfully. I opened my mouth again and as more air entered my lungs fiercely, I shut my mouth tight with my teeth because my open lips were tearing apart with the speed of the wind. With my mouth shut and hands flung open and legs thrown back, I was now in a birdlike position. Not that I made any effort to get in position but after the drama of the fall, the body instinctively finds its place in the universe. I sped down and for the first time I experienced gravity. The earth was not letting me go anywhere. It would pull me towards it even if the pull meant killing me. We are all bound by that same gravity through our possessive and obsessive behaviors. Gravity, like attachment, is the way of the universe. Detachment is not the way of the universe, and any attempt towards it is only a temporary victory.

The two stars, Uma and Karlos, were shining below me and then they suddenly disappeared. A few seconds had passed or maybe minutes. When you fall from the sky the only time that you know is eternity.

My form was stable and the initial fright had lessened. The fall was making me nauseated and the stretch in my body was painful. I could barely breathe and I was making every effort to stay alert and in control. I stretched my right arm down and looked at my watch. It was 7,000 feet and the needle was ticking fast. When it reached past 5,500 feet I moved my arm and struggled to catch hold of my back. With every second that passed I was losing altitude and I was beginning to panic. It was an effort to fight the wind and finally my hand grasped the ball and tugged. Almost in an instant I felt a tug and flutter behind my ears, and in one painful tug on the middle of my legs and back, I had stopped falling. The parachute was open and I could see two fluorescent green umbrellas just a few feet below me. I looked up and my parachute was green too.

Descending in a parachute was not as frightening as the fall from the sky but it certainly was more painful. My whole body was hanging through the harness and the gravity was not helping. It was cold and the wind was raging through my nose into my lungs. My nose was stinging. The only good part about all of this rush was that I was flying in the night sky 4000 feet above ground level or maybe sea level and right now both didn't matter. I felt like a bird. I felt connected with the universe. It was almost as if I was exploring the skies. The feeling of gliding in a parachute is a hundred times more divine than looking out of an aircraft window. You are IN THE SKY. You are no longer looking at the sky. The moon was on my left and I could see it with a clarity I had never seen before. I saw a flock of geese flying below. "Get out of my way," I mentally screamed.

The drop was a high speed one. I thought the parachute might have been a sail but it was a speed ride. At the speed that I was descending, I knew that I would certainly break my bones with the landing. So how did one land? Maybe I could start running in the air as the land came closer and that way I could run and save myself the thud. I had seen that in the movies, commandos running as they touched down. But as the ground came closer my horror grew. There was no land, there were only dense trees. I saw one parachute straighten up and disappear into the 'land' and then the other disappeared and then it was my turn as I headed straight for the trees.

"God no! Help!" I shouted. I could shout! I had my voice back and I would create the greatest ruckus and let the whole Malaysian forest know that I had arrived.

I broke through the treetops and the branches split as they cut through my arms and my legs. I stopped screaming. In my frantic attempt to stop falling I caught hold of a branch, which creaked as I tugged it and broke as I fell down further, this time much slower. The parachute was entangled at the treetop and now I hung in mid-air about 10 feet above the ground. My cheeks were bruised and so were my arms and legs. Only my back that was covered by the parachute bag was safe but hurting from the arch of the fall. I was bruised and cut and I was hurt.

"Karlos," I shouted instinctively. "Uma," I called out. I was in pain but there was something bigger than my pain and that was my purpose of being there. So instead of wailing about my wounds I shouted out for Karlos and Uma.

There was only silence. I had seen the two parachutes nearby so they could not be far away. My harness was hurting and I tried to tug at the ropes but the parachute was entangled in the branches and did not give way.

I swore I heard a voice and I started to shout again. "Uma . . . Karlos . . ." I heard Uma's voice first; she was calling out to me.

I started to tug at my parachute violently and with one large crash the branch above me broke and I fell down 10 feet with a shower of broken branches on my head. I was lucky not to have broken any bones. Branches kept raining down on the parachute until there was silence again. The ground was moist and I was entangled and trapped inside the parachute. I was shivering with the adrenaline rush and I could now hear Uma close by. "Uma," I shouted until I heard her really close.

It was a relief to hear her voice and feel her hand on me. Both of us worked to get me out of the maze of ropes until finally I was free. I unhooked the bag from the ropes; the food was squashed but I didn't care.

Uma looked pitiful and I guess I did too. Muddied and bloody-faced, with bruised arms and bleeding legs, we had no time and no recourse to medical aid. "Where is Karlos ?" Uma asked.

He had to be close.

Uma and I walked half a mile in circles I guess, shouting Karlos' name but there was no answer. My wounds were stinging but the urgency of finding Karlos kept us both going without complaint. We saw a dozen gleaming eyes of nocturnal animals that appeared inquisitively and disappeared hurriedly into the dark. There were fluttering of wings, barks and howls, and all sorts of night-time sounds. The forest was rich in its nocturnal life. Uma and I clutched each other as we bravely continued our search for Karlos.

And then we found him, a few feet ahead. We could see his parachute stuck in the trees and Karlos lying on the ground next to a tree trunk, unconscious. A curious mongoose darted out of the way as we approached.

We both ran towards Karlos. I picked up his head and slapped his cheeks trying to get him back to consciousness, while Uma began to unstrap him from his harness. Karlos opened his eyes feebly only to close them again. Something had happened to Karlos. He was not speaking, maybe he had broken a bone or broken his back or maybe he was having a heart attack. "Karlos, what happened?" I shook him and slapped his face again, this time gently.

Karlos opened his eyes and tried to speak. I could not understand. It was all garbled. We needed to get him some help.

"We need to get help," I told Uma urgently as I held Karlos' head and placed it on my lap. I did not know what to do to make him feel better. This had been my fear all along. I could have jumped and died and the story would have been over. But how do you take the journey forward when one member of your team or family falls down? When one goes down, by default everyone goes down. We were here on a mission and now a different mission had taken form - to save Karlos' life. Every time I have gotten on track with my life and every time I have been convinced I was in the right direction, a tragedy showed up and altered the course of my journey. This, however, was not the time for my frustration; a man was lying helpless in my lap and I had to get him some help.

Uma got up and said, "I will go and get some help." As she moved her foot to walk, I grabbed it and she almost fell.

"What are you doing?" she shouted, regaining her balance.

"You are not going anywhere. We stick together. We need to get help for Karlos together," I said, reminding her of Kurt's instructions.

"But what do we do with him? The man is near unconscious. You wait here, I will get help," Uma protested. Normally that would have been the logical thing to do but we had strict instructions to stick together and Uma was suggesting we break the rule. Obviously Kurt would have anticipated accidents and there must be a reason for his instructions. My thinking was that if Uma got lost, or caught, then we all were doomed. There was no way of communicating, so the only way out was to stay together.

"Fine," Uma said, and I finally let go of her foot.

"Let's pick him up," I suggested. It would be daybreak soon and we would be able to get some help. Maybe he would be better by then. Sometimes it's the shock that hits us, and as much as Karlos was trying to be brave, I knew he was afraid.

We got Karlos to sit up and he laid his head on Uma's shoulder. Reaching through his grogginess, we told Karlos that we would be picking him up and if anything hurt he should let us know. It was a backbreaking task to get Karlos to his feet. The man was as heavy as any tree could have been. He tried to walk, or rather to limp, and we had to drag him most of the time.

The trees were woven dense and but for the moonlight, we would have been disoriented. We did not know which direction to take. I suppose when you are lost, any direction works as long as you are on the move. We decided to move downhill because that would be easier.

Just a few meters into our trek and we were exhausted. Through the trees I saw a flash of light in the distance. "Did you see that Uma?" I asked her in a whisper as we came to an abrupt halt.

"See what?" Uma said.

I craned my neck in the direction of the light and there it was, a distinct point of light. "There, can you see that light?" I pointed in the direction.

"Yes." Uma jumped, letting go of Karlos and almost dropping him over me. Karlos groaned.

"Here, hold on to him," Uma said, releasing Karlos' weight on me, "I will go and get help."

"Uma!" I growled in the tone I use when my dogs misbehave and I need to get their attention. "Stick together. Hold on to Karlos, we are getting there. It's just a few meters away."

Uma was sullen but complied anyway.

We were in a foreign land. We had no identity and no money. Help could prove fatal if we landed in the hands of wrong people. With Karlos injured, we had landed ourselves in extreme crisis. Uma did not understand the gravity of the situation. I had to practically carry an oversized man whose life was in my hands. Then there was a naïve young girl whose carelessness could cost us all our lives. This team was mismatched from the start. Team members should be an asset but here every member was a liability and my purpose, like theirs, was sidelined for the moment.

After a few minutes of backbreaking misery, we arrived at a small clearing. It was strange that a cottage would be built here in the middle of the forest. I was cautious and beckoned Uma to remain silent.

"You sit here with Karlos. Watch my back. I am going to the cottage to check if we can get help. But first I want to make sure that we are not leading ourselves into trouble. Keep your eyes on me, don't leave me if anything goes wrong," I told Uma very sternly, looking into her eyes, making sure that she understood.

Uma looked as if she wanted to throw back the 'we stick together' rule at me but she nodded her agreement for the moment anyway. Karlos was conscious now and was obviously in pain. "Give him the beer—maybe that will revive him," I winked at Uma.

I walked towards the cottage cautiously from behind the trees. What was a cottage doing here in the middle of the forest? There was a light on inside and there were two large windows with no curtains on the front and a large metal-framed door. I walked from behind the stone cottage. I could see the chimney was smoking. Someone was awake inside. The villagers are usually early risers but I did not want to take a chance. With no sign of anyone from the outside I came to the front of the cottage. I could see Uma and Karlos from there and Uma was looking at me with her hands folded, half covering her face. She was making me nervous. Actually I *was* nervous. I was a part of Kurt's insanity and now I was no longer acting to cover up my $25,000; I was acting to save Karlos' life.

I stood on my toes and peeped into the cottage. As I quickly glanced around the room I saw a young, native girl squatting by a fireplace that had a kettle on it. She looked like she was in her teens, slim and fairly attractive. There was a large bed on the side but no one lay on it. My eyes scanned the cottage, which seemed quite like a studio apartment. It was empty except for the young girl. There was a door in the corner, a very slender door, which I assumed was the toilet.

My toes hurt but before I could hop back on my foot, I heard Uma cry out. In that same instant a hand grabbed my shoulder. I died a thousand deaths. My heart stopped beating as I turned around and came face to face with a short, fat woman. Her hair was wet and she had a towel on her shoulder. She said something in a foreign dialect and I was relieved that she was not attacking me. I didn't know what to say and started blabbering.

"My friend is hurt . . . " I pointed towards Uma and Karlos. "We need to get him some help. Can you help please?" I was trembling like a leaf.

The woman looked confused. She continued to speak and I didn't know whether she was abusing me, accusing me of trespassing or offering to help. But since she was not attacking me I thought of taking my chances and asking her for help. I had to do something. I had to lead her to do something before she did something I didn't want her to do.

I pointed towards Uma and started to walk in her direction, signaling to the woman to walk with me. She hesitated for a few seconds and then followed me. I sprinted towards Uma who sat clutching Karlos. The woman took a look at him and let out a cry. She sat down by his side and took his hand. She said something to me that I did not understand. She motioned to Uma to pick him up and the three of us carried him towards the cottage. Karlos was still conscious.

The young girl inside the cottage was now standing at the door and looked totally baffled by our presence. It seemed to me that she had not seen foreigners before. She stared at us in utter disbelief, her eyes anxiously searching the forest to see if more of us would follow.

The woman got to work instantly. She inspected Karlos, who was now lying on the floor near the fireplace. She pointed to his rib and his hip joint. Maybe that was broken or fractured but I could not understand what she was saying. While the woman tended to Karlos, Uma pulled me aside and whispered, "We need to find Bomo, the keeper of the future, and get the message." I could not believe that Uma was suggesting that we leave Karlos behind and move on.

I stared at Uma with total disgust. I don't know what emotions crossed my heart. I wanted to think of her as mean, self centered, selfish, and half a dozen more labels, but before I could despise her for her suggestion, I remembered all the occasions when I had left one of my parents or my brother sick at home because I had work to do at the office or I had to fly off to a seminar. I had never ever stayed back to tend to my loved ones when they needed me. My commitment to my work had always been greater than my love for my family. My mother often joked that even if she was dying, I would still fly off to do my work rather than be by her side. And what was worse was that I had never corrected her view. Today, instead of thinking badly of Uma, I felt really small in my own eyes. Often when we spot shortcomings in others, they are but reflections of our own.

Karlos began to breathe very heavily and he kept looking straight at me. What does he want me to do? Does he want to say something? I bent over and held his hand. "You will be fine." I tried to stay composed. In looking after Karlos I was secretly making up for all my neglect towards my family.

The woman brought a dozen eggs and sat down besides Karlos, almost pushing me away. She placed some on Karlos' chest and began to bandage them on. Holy cow! This was no time for some mumbo jumbo, I thought. This woman was out of her mind. The man needed help and she was sticking eggs on him. She kept mumbling something as she worked. It sounded like "Karlos is possessed and I need to get the devil away."

Karlos was struggling to breathe and I was beginning to panic. His eyes were becoming static and his breath slower and heavier.

No. . . no. Please don't die on me. Please don't die. Not now. Not like this. Fight, Karlos. Nothing has happened to you. Don't die. Don't die please. I pleaded to his soul for Karlos was staring blankly at me.

And then it happened . . . Karlos seemed to stop breathing. I wanted to thump his chest and revive him but that stupid fat woman caught my hand tightly. She put her finger on her lips and looked around at the room as if she could see his soul. This woman was utterly insane. I needed to beat his chest, break the bloody eggs, maybe pump some air into his mouth but she was in control here. I thought if I fought and pissed her off she might turn us all in. And if Karlos was dead, then we were all in deep, deep trouble.

"Karlos," I spoke out loud. I could feel Uma's grip tighten on my shoulder and her nails digging into my skin. Karlos was not responding. Karlos was not breathing and he was not blinking. Karlos was dead.

We both sat there as the woman covered his face with the cloth the young girl had used to lift the kettle off the fire. This woman obviously had some screws loose. But what were our choices?

"Are we going to get arrested? Will they call the police?" Uma asked in panic. The woman instantly jumped on hearing the word Police. She said something aloud angrily, which had the word police three times in it. She stepped outside keeping an eye on us lest we run away with the dead body and called out to someone. The young girl ran out of the house. I got up and tried to calm her down, telling her not to call the police, that we were tourists, out trekking, and how our friend got hurt and we just needed help.

Uma was pulling at my arm. "Lets run. We need to find Bomo and get the message and get to the airport," she said with alarm.

Now the word Bomo seemed to have hit off another alarm button with the woman as she started a whole string of accusations with the word Bomo sprinkled in it half a dozen times. What was I going to do? I wished I was dead instead of Karlos. What a great team I had! One was dead and the other was trying to get me killed.

The woman entered the house and lifted the cloth from Karlos' face. I did not see if Karlos' eyes were already closed or she had closed them. And before I knew it, Uma broke into a run.

"Uma," I shouted as she ran out of the house as fast as her legs could carry her. I didn't know whether to run behind her—maybe the woman would attack us all for leaving a dead man in her custody. "Uma," I roared as Uma disappeared into the trees and I stood at the door of the cottage with tears in my eyes.

This was turning into the worst nightmare of my life. I had come here for a mission. One member of my team had died and another had abandoned me. What was I supposed to do? I was in a crazy house with a woman who had plastered Karlos with eggs and was threatening to call the police. I was ruined. I was going to break down. I began to sob and soon broke into loud howls. I was tired and I was hurting. My own pain began to take over. My wounds were swollen and I wanted to go home.

The woman came over and laid a mat on the floor and beckoned me to sit on it and with a warm wet cloth began to wipe my wounds. She spoke something in a kind tone and though the cloth stung I let her do what she was doing. Maybe she would wrap me in some eggs too, who knows, and maybe I will die too. I sat there while the lady tied my toes to each other with a grass like thread making a web. The pain from my bruises magically receded.

In a few minutes the woman got up. She tied her hair back and picked up a cloth bag. She said something to the girl and they both moved out of the cottage. I could not stand up for fear of destroying the little web that she had made on my toes.

Karlos lay there, very still. My vision was beginning to blur. And then suddenly it hit me: I could make a phone call. I could call Kurt. I could call him and tell him about our problem. I had the phone. I had almost forgotten about it. I frantically opened the little jacket bag and I took out the phone with shaking hands. Kurt's number was easy to remember and I was thankful that I could still recall it. I dialed the number and just as before Kurt answered the phone on the first ring.

"Kurt?" I said before he completed his "Hello".

"Yes, Kurt Rinck," he sounded indifferent. He did not bother to ask how we were or whether we survived the jump.

"Kurt, we are in the forest of Genting Highlands. Karlos is dead. He did not survive the jump and Uma has abandoned the mission. She has run away. I don't know what to do. You need to get me some help here. Karlos is dead. I'm in a small cottage in the forest. Whoever is coming here can find us where the fluorescent parachutes are." I spoke rapidly in one breath, trying to control the tremor in my voice and fighting back my tears. This was no time for emotions; if there was a time to take control, it was now. It was easy to take control of the stage, my talk and the audience's reaction. But the true test of my courage was now.

"I want Karlos alive," Kurt barked on the other end. "Find Uma, do your job and get to the airport. Do you understand?"

No, I did not understand. I wanted to tell Kurt that I did not understand his insane ways and that this was utterly ridiculous. Karlos was dead and Uma had fled into the jungle and I had a task to do. I needed some advice and help and instead he was telling me what I didn't want to hear. I wanted to tell Kurt I did not understand but before I could make my opinion clear, he hung up!

I hated Kurt. With all my might and all I had, I hated Kurt. He just hung up. The fat rascal knew this was my only call. I could have called the President and maybe he would have helped. I could have called my father and maybe he could have helped. But Kurt hung up. Actually I don't think my father or the President could have helped, but Kurt certainly could have and he didn't! Damn him.

How could I bring a dead man alive? Karlos' body lay there. I didn't even know how to mourn for the man. I didn't even know him. I could feel his spirit fill the room and I was beginning to get scared. I had never sat alone with a dead body before or, for that matter, I had never even seen one. This was the scariest moment of my life.

I did not want to look in Karlos' direction. I knew he was dead but I did not want to acknowledge that. I wondered who would feel his loss. He had said he was single but I was sure he had a family. I wondered what this would do to Kurt's reputation and I wondered what this would do to me.

My body felt limp and I could no longer feel the pain from my wounds. I lay down on the mat, frightfully close to Karlos' body. I just closed my eyes to rest them and to wait till the woman returned. She had us both captive anyway. In an instant I fell asleep.

CHAPTER 6

Bomo - Keeper of The Future

I must have slept for many long hours because when I awoke there was no trace of daylight outside. I figured the sun had set while I slept next to a dead Karlos.

The woman and the little girl had returned home and were talking frantically to a very scary looking man. He was clearly Malaysian and looked like a gangster. Maybe he was here to kidnap us or to bury Karlos. Seeing me awake, the woman bent forward and got the web off my toes with a snap. I was surprised that I did not feel any pain whatsoever. I didn't quite understand how that web of wild medicinal herbs had healed my wounds but I felt better and for the moment that was all that mattered.

The man now walked towards me. He was short and overweight. He had the smallest eyes I had ever seen and large gaps in his teeth. He wore a very loose soiled white shirt and soiled white pants. He must have been roaming the jungles, I thought. He bent towards me and beckoned me to move away. As I moved away, he plopped himself on the mat where I was lying. I was no longer afraid. I had nothing to fear. The woman meant me no harm. You don't heal someone only to kill him or her later.

The man was now tending to Karlos. I sat up to watch as he started to take the bandages off. "It is not his time to die," he spoke in surprisingly good English.

What did he mean it was not his time to die? Did he not know that the man had been dead for over eight hours? These were facts but the man was oblivious, obviously at work. He removed all the bandages that the woman had so meticulously tied on Karlos. The eggs started to roll aside but to my surprise, none of them cracked. As he handed the bundle of unwrapped bandages to the woman, a stench welled up. The man picked up one of the eggs and cracked it. It was hard-boiled! He cut the egg with a large knife that the woman had given him. The hard-boiled sections split apart to reveal two large, rusted needles inside.

How did the needles get inside the egg? And how was the egg hard-boiled?

The woman seemed as aghast as I was. I translated her excited gestures to indicate: "See, this is what I was doing with the eggs! Capturing evil in them!" The man kept cracking the eggs; all of which were hard-boiled, and had rusted needles in them. I picked up one egg on the side and inspected it. There was no visible crack or pinhole on it. Its shell was sealed tight. I cracked it by hitting it slightly on the floor. It was a real egg and it was hard-boiled. As I tried to rip the boiled egg open with my bare hands a pin pricked my finger and I let out a cry. As a drop of blood flowed out of my finger, the man, woman and girl simultaneously let out a cry as well. The man took my hand violently and pressed it onto Karlos' body and let out what sounded to me like a string of curses. He pressed my hand hard on Karlos' leg, which felt warm. How could he be warm if he was dead?

I was horrified when Karlos moved a toe. This man was bringing a dead man to life. I felt faint.

The gangster-man looked delighted. "It is not his time to die!" he repeated again, looking at me with pride. "He thinks all the time that he will die, so he attracts untimely death. All the time he fears he will die. Every time he is alone, he wishes that he is dead. So with little injury he brings untimely death," the man explained to me and then to the old lady.

"This needle in the egg is bad energy from the man. These needles make his brain bad and now they are in the egg. Now all the bad in him is out in the egg. He will be alive," he continued.

Karlos moved and groaned and coughed. If I had to explain what had just happened here, I had no answer except that it had happened. It seemed that all of the negative energy and fear of death had been drawn out of Karlos into the hard-boiled eggs and rusty needles. I was not sure if the eggs had already been boiled with the needles inside, or if they had really become hard-boiled because of the bad energy. Had the needles just appeared inside as a symbol of warding off untimely death? It was hard to theorize but I had heard that the Genting Highlands was the land of black magic and sorcery. I was shocked at what had happened and was a little apprehensive. Was this really Karlos or had they attracted some other spirit to take over his body? I think I was finally losing it, becoming a part of these people's mad ways. But whatever it was, real or imaginary, my pain was gone, my wounds felt better, and Karlos was alive.

The man now seemed to own Karlos. He kept close to him and asked him to repeat some weird mumbo jumbo which seemed quite like harassment for a man who had just woken up from the dead. I tried to talk to Karlos but he was in the man's custody and too weak to make conversation. He occasionally mumbled, "I want to go home," and the man would reply, "You are home, my Lord."

After a ceremonious celebration, which was marked by clapping of hands and chanting, the man offered his respects for the last time and left the cottage. The woman began cooking something that smelt really horrible. She offered it to Karlos and I waited to be served. It was horrible stuff but it seemed rude to chew on squashed candy and refuse food offered by the woman who had just saved our lives. "Karlos," I said, trying to get Karlos' attention. He seemed to be in quite a daze. "I am happy you are fine." I took his hand in mine. He seemed confused that I thought something was wrong with him. I decided to drop the subject. "We have to find Bomo, the keeper of the future. We have to get the message and get to the airport tomorrow. We are going to make it." I tried to get him back on track.

"I want to go home," was his only response.

What was I going to do? Karlos was alive and wanted to go home. There was no sign of Uma. I guess Karlos was going to quit. Kurt had told me to find Uma and now I had the dirty work of bringing her back from her own cowardice. I decided to do that in the morning. Maybe the fat lady would let us sleep in the cottage for the night. She had not mentioned anything about us leaving or getting out yet and I decided not to bring that up.

"I want to meet Bomo, the keeper of the future," I said to the lady. "Do you know how I can find him?" I suddenly realized my stupidity.

The gangster-man had spoken English; I should have asked him this question. But I had been so taken aback with the whole process of reviving Karlos that it had not struck me. Now he was gone. I somehow had to reach Bomo, but first I had to reach out to the woman and make her understand.

"Bomo," I said slowly, "I want to meet Bomo."

"Bomo," the woman nodded excitedly. She understood. She went outside and called the young girl. She started the sentence with Bomo and now the young girl made an action and pointed towards Karlos, suggesting that the man who visited us and got Karlos back was Bomo.

I had not felt so stupid in a long time. Bomo was in the house a few minutes ago. I had been assigned the task of meeting him and I had slipped up. It is uncanny how what we want is really within our grasp but sometimes we don't have the ability to recognize that. Our wish-fulfilling genie manifests in clever ways and we don't know we were in its company until after it has left. When we desire something, the process of its manifestation starts instantly. The question is, 'Will you recognize the opportunity or will you let it go out of your own ignorance?' In this case, I had already let it go.

If you start tracing your success backwards you will realize that it all started when you planted your intention. Every person who comes in your life becomes a part of your life. That person has a very important role to play in your success. If Karlos had not fallen ill, we would not have come to the cottage, the lady would not have called Bomo, Karlos would not have been saved, and I would never have found Bomo. Everything made sense and everything always makes sense if we want it to. Otherwise, life can be seen as a random sequence of events, the way Uma saw it. When we stick together and connect the dots, we win.

"I want to see Bomo," I now tried to explain to the young girl. She seemed smarter and sharper than the fat woman and she understood instantly. She pointed towards the forest and said, "Bomo."

I was delighted. She knew where Bomo was; I needed her to guide me. I took her hand. "Take me to Bomo," I said, pointing in the direction she showed me.

The girl looked back at her mother, who nodded her permission and disappeared into the house. The girl stood still as I tugged at her and the woman appeared again with two lamps in her hand. With the moon behind the clouds it was dark; the lamps would come in handy. We set off with the girl walking ahead of me. We zigzagged about a hundred meters into the trees and then she suddenly stopped and smiled and pointed towards a tree, saying "Bomo."

I was confused. Bomo was a tree? I pointed to the tree and questioned her, "Bomo?" and she excitedly nodded her head.

I did not understand. I thought Bomo was a person. I thought Bomo was the man who had visited the house. That's what the lady and even this young woman had implied. And now she was pulling a fast one on me and telling me that Bomo was a tree. I was getting irritated.

Confusion is a dangerous state of mind. If left unattended and unguarded it can lead to rage and anger and sometimes even murder. Ask any terrorist about how it all started and you will find that at the start he was just a confused little boy. I decided to take charge of my confusion and sort it right there.

I took the lamp and walked towards the tree. I began to inspect it. Maybe it was a talking tree. Maybe the future was hidden in its bark. The girl started to laugh. I turned around and she pointed to a place before the tree and repeated, "Bomo."

I traced my steps back to carefully judge the place between her and the tree, and find the exact spot she had pointed to. When I reached that spot, I pointed towards that nothingness and said, "Bomo" and she nodded in agreement with a delight that I had finally found him.

So Bomo was thin air. Before I had completed that thought I felt a tight slap on my face. I was so shocked the lamp fell out of my hand and with a distinct sizzle the flame died out. Now I was convinced that Bomo was a ghost. I had felt the slap on my face. It was real. Either Bomo was invisible or I needed to get out of there. Before I could run back to the cottage, a form appeared out of nowhere.

It was the same man who had come to the cottage. "Sorry for the slap," he said apologetically. "I forgot I was in the future. You could not see me. Sorry again," he said as he tried to touch my cheek. I wanted to tell him to spare me the eggs lest he bandaged my cheeks with them, but he just touched my cheek gently with his fingertip and the sting went away.

The man was invisible. I had just seen an invisible man. He appeared right in front of my eyes. "You were in the future?" I tried to ignore his abrupt arrival into the present.

"Yes, I keep the future," he said, delighted that I knew.

"Whose future do you keep?" I was curious.

"All the future" he said, waving his hands as though to tell me that he kept the future of the whole universe.

I laughed and Bomo frowned. I didn't mean to offend him; I just found it cute that he kept the future of the world. The man was dangerous-looking but sounded funny and spoke English with a funny accent. He did the disappearing act and was convincing me that he kept the future of the world. It's a pity how we often judge others by their looks and outward appearance. Just because she looks good, she must be a good person and just because he laughs he must be happy. Looks have nothing to do with goodness and possessions have nothing to do with riches and laughter, nothing to do with happiness. Yet we make these stupid equations in our head and live a convenient life of never having to learn the truth.

Bomo was an impatient man. "Come, I can show you," he said as he took my hand. "Which future you want to see?" he asked like a teenager about to show off his new bike.

"My future," I smiled and he smiled back as though this would be a tough one to show. The man had quite a sense of humor. He said something excitedly to the young girl who nodded and darted back towards the cottage. Much to my dismay, she took her lamp with her.

"Are you ready for your future?" he asked as he tugged my hand, pulling me towards him.

"What the . . ." and before I could complete my sentence I had walked through a wall of a jelly-like substance. I came out on the other side in broad daylight. I saw Bomo standing next to me. What was this? Had I traveled into the future? Oh my God! Bomo had taken me to the future.

It seemed like we were in a countryside of northern India. I saw a small beaten-down house that had a pickup truck parked outside. There were dogs barking in the backyard and a man was sleeping on the garden bench with a newspaper on his face to block the sun. A plump woman in her late forties emerged. She looked a lot like me. She looked older than her age and I frowned. She wore worn out ill fitting clothes. She seemed like she did nothing productive; the bored and indifferent look on her face said it all. "Is this my future?" I muttered.

"You don't like it?" Bomo read my disappointment.

"This can never be me!" I exclaimed. "are you out of your mind Bomo? Wasted and fat and ugly like her?" I pointed accusingly to the version of a wasted, fat and ugly me emerging from the house.

Bomo looked at me apologetically as the fat lady began to shout at her even more wasted husband. She was accusing her husband for being 'good for nothing' and obviously missing to spot that in herself.

"Ok, look there," he said, getting my attention on the other side of the road. As I looked on the other side, I saw a high-rise building. I spun around and the beaten down house had disappeared. "What the heck!" I muttered again.

A woman emerged from a chauffeur driven car, slim and stern. That was me. . . er . . . she . . . er . . . me walking towards the building. I was obviously someone important but this whole set up of the chauffeur driven car and walking in a stuck up manner towards an office in a concrete jungle gave me the shivers.

"No," I shouted aloud. I would never ever be so stuck up in life. I would never trade my time and effort for earning a life like that. I looked stern and mean, like a corporate shark. I never wanted to be like that. I was a fun loving and adventurous person. I had given up every opportunity of trading my freedom to the slavery of the corporate world and here I was exactly the person I had dreaded to become. "No," I said again, driving the thought of that future out of my head.

"You don't like it?" Now Bomo looked disappointed.

He turned me around and I saw another scene. It was my house, my current house, worn out, different dogs, used BMW, and a tired me. My mother was nowhere around and I was obviously alone.

"No!" I said out aloud. Now this was not even a future, it was a nightmare! Why would I be worse off in the future than I was today? I had aspired for a bigger house, more cars and more friends. What Bomo was showing me was a deteriorated image of my present, in the future. With what I saw it didn't seem like I had made any progress. I could not imagine a life without progress but maybe with my current state of mind and being, there was a slight possibility I could lead myself there.

"Ok." Bomo sighed at my disappointment.

He took my hand and tugged me forward. We were now in a hospital and I was lying on the ICU bed, hooked onto life support. I had overdosed on prescribed drugs.

What was Bomo doing? Why was he showing me one disastrous future after another? I hated hospitals. It was my greatest fear to end up in the hospital. It took all my courage for me to go to the dentist and here Bomo was showing me a full-blown scene of me in the ICU. It seemed that I was suffering from acute stress and depression. I was working insane hours and my work did not benefit me. An overdose of anti-anxiety pills and anti-depressants had led me to the ICU. I had tried to sort out the chaos in my life through drugs, which had done what they were meant to; kill me!

"No, Bomo," I protested, almost threateningly. I knew I would never drive my life to the point where I had to depend upon drugs to sort my reality out.

"Sorry," Bomo waved his hands and took me yet a step forward.

We were now sitting on the sofa in a plush suburban apartment where we could hear loud screams. Before I could get a grip of where I was, a glass smashed in the room inside and out stormed an angry and bitter looking woman, sobbing violently. She looked like a well maintained me in her early forties. "I hate you," she said to the man there, her husband.

"No, Bomo," I said, frightened, as I tried to walk towards the door and run out. This woman was an emotional wreck and I had known this kind of women up close and personal. They were the rich wives of unfaithful husbands, with their private lives in a mess. With no productive use of their own lives, they lived to survive the misery their busy husbands brought them. I would never be like that.

"No?" Bomo asked innocently as he opened the door of the apartment to let me out. As soon as we stepped out, tears began to roll down my cheeks. Was this my future? What was Bomo trying to tell me?

"Look," Bomo whispered. We were now on the top of a hill. I could see a dainty house, like the one I had always dreamt of. Horses grazed in the expansive farm as a couple of dogs chased each other. A helicopter came purring down and landed in a little clearing not far from the cottage. I walked out with a gorgeous man holding a little girl, our daughter.

"Wow," I said. "That is my future." I almost clapped my hands in delight. I had always wanted a house on a mountain with a huge farm and lots of animals and open space. I wanted to live in the countryside, under the open skies and in a place where I would have a glimpse of the whole universe. I could see the ocean in the distance, the sky above and the earth under my feet. I lived where the eagles soared and the clouds touched my feet. As for work, my chopper got me to work three times a week; the other four days I spent with my family in total bliss. "This is my future," I smiled at Bomo almost jumping with delight.

"No," Bomo said, shattering my dream, and we found ourselves back in the dark forest.

That was so rude, I thought. Just when I was beginning to like what I saw and just when I had finally got a glimpse of my future as I wanted it, Bomo crash-landed me back to reality. I almost wanted to bop his head but it was so dark that I could only see the white of his eyes and his teeth.

"Your future is only a possibility. So all that you saw, everything, can be your future. Everything is possible." Bomo spoke with great wisdom that only the keeper of the future could know.

"Future is a possibility that you create today," he spoke slowly so I could understand clearly.

"What you do today, what you choose today, will become your tomorrow. So you can choose your fate," he said with a frown.

"If you want to be wasted, waste your life today. Make excuses, miss opportunities and you will be the fat woman with a useless husband," he said, reminding me of the first picture I saw.

"Live for money. Keep material gains over personal mastery and you will be the iron woman in the iron cage," he explained. "Use alcohol as a solution for stress, pop pills to drown your loneliness and you will be in a hospital. Sleep with other men behind your husband's back and you will be the bitter ugly woman you saw. Or . . ." he paused, "grow and enrich your soul and follow your heart while serving others and you will become worthy of your own desires. They will manifest to serve you and everyone else you invite into your life. Which future you will keep? It is your choice depending on the person you choose to become every single day of your life!"

I was stumped. I had met the keeper of the future and he had shown me the key to keep mine. I could choose. I could choose my future and then work backwards and work my way out.

If I wanted that house on the hilltop with the chopper as my ride, I had to work hard to deserve it. I had to serve more and contribute more. And to serve more and contribute more, I had to become more. To deserve that man, who would be the father of my children, I had to learn to nurture, to be respectful, tolerant, grounded, balanced, empowering, and supportive. I had to become deserving of a bigger future. Today was my chance to create it. Consciously. Every decision I took, every choice I made would need to pass the test: Is this in alignment with my future?

"Your future is never about what you have, it is about who you become as a result of all you want to have!" Bomo spoke, breaking into my thoughts.

"Wait, I have something for you," Bomo said and he pulled me back towards him. I smashed again through the jelly-like wall. We were back in the future, my future, in the house on the mountainside. Bomo opened the gate of the majestic villa and took me inside. Bomo was running, holding my hand tight as he rushed into the house, almost bursting through the main door. We ran up the stairs directly, without stopping to take a tour of the lower section of the house. Bomo was obviously in a hurry. We rushed up to the first floor. Bomo opened the door of the first room that we came to. The future me, was in the master bedroom. I was in bed with my man. We were wrapped in white silken sheets, my head resting on his shoulder as he kissed my forehead. We looked so much in love; we looked so much at peace. We looked like soul mates, like eternal companions, like we were meant for each other, like we were divine creations. As I looked at myself looking into his eyes, I could feel the love I had so yearned for. This was it. This was real. This was my future. I gasped as the man held my hand and slipped a ring on my finger. "Will you be my companion for eternity?" he proposed in the most profoundly spiritual way. Bomo and I stood by the bedside watching me break into tears as I said, "I will, beyond eternity." I wore the ring and I slipped into his arms and became one with the man I loved so dearly. Bomo walked over and pulled the ring off my finger as I lay in the man's embrace. Holding the ring in his hand he tugged at me, whispering, "Let's go!"

We sneaked out of the room, down the stairs. As Bomo opened the main door, I banged into the jelly wall again. The man should at least warn me when we cross realities. Bomo was reckless, I thought.

"Here it is." He thrust the ring in my hand. "A memento from your future," he smiled.

I held the ring tightly in my hand. It was real. In the dark, the diamond shone and lit up points in the forest. It was real. This was a freaking expensive diamond ring. It was a real ring. My future was real. I was shaking all over, with joy or disbelief I could not tell. I had seen my future and I had evidence of it, right here in my hands.

"And one more thing," Bomo said as he disappeared for a few seconds and came back with a lamp. "I got this from the old wasted lady," he chuckled "For you to go back home."

I took the lamp from Bomo's hand, shivering from the evidence of another potential future, and looked around for the light of the cottage as my reference to find my way back.

"Thank you, Bomo," I said, but Bomo was already shaking his head.

"Your future is shaped by the choices you make in the present. Live each day with care. I watch you in the present and based on what you do today, I start defining possibilities for your future. Right now you are headed for disaster; the ICU would be a close bet. But you can change it. You can have any future you want. Where do you begin? Here. When do you start? Now. Where are your possibilities? Within you. Watch every step you take, for you are heading towards the future: you can either land up there accidently and then pretend you don't know how you got there, or design it carefully by the choices you make. You have evidence of both right now," he said pointing to the lamp and the ring that now adorned my finger. He chuckled and before I could say anything, Bomo had already gone back to the future.

I took the lamp and traced my way back to the cottage. It was an easy find. I guess if you have a point of light in the distance, no matter how dark the path is, that one point of light is enough to get you through.

The cottage was in darkness inside. Darn, everyone had gone to sleep. I shuddered at the thought of sleeping outside. As I approached the door in the darkness, with the light from the lamp creating some scary shadows in the background, I saw that the door to the cottage was slightly ajar. They had kept it open for me. I sighed with relief.

Inside it seemed like a pyjama party. The fat lady and her daughter were cuddled on the big bed and Karlos was lying on the same mat, at the same spot where he lay dead earlier. There was another mat a few feet away from him, which I assumed was for me. With no clothes to change into, I decided to just lie down and try to sleep. I was wide awake though. How can you sleep when you have just seen your future, the one you don't want and also the one you have desired from your heart?

I lay down staring at the ceiling and then sat up with a start. I had to fill the journal before I ended my day, and to be honest I was quite excited to write. It was like discovering a new perspective to how I had lived my life that day.

I walked out with my journal and sat on the doorstep outside with the lamp by my side.

I began to write:

For the longest time my greatest fear was that I would lose. And here I am. I have nothing with me. Nothing at all except direction. And with nothing in my pocket and no certainty about my whereabouts I have met with the most magical people I could ever imagine. And since I have nothing to lose and my mind is free of that fear, I am able to see things that I have never seen before. I am able to think in a manner that I have never thought before. In losing all fear of losing I have found my ability to really live.

I have seen a man come back from the dead. And I saw how I was moving in the wrong direction of life. I will never be able to understand how Bomo brought Karlos back to life and I will never be able to understand how I was even living until now, as I did.

In hating Uma I caught a glimpse of how reckless I had been towards my family's needs. Sometimes being there for people and standing by them is a greater purpose of mankind.

Bomo was there even when I did not recognize him. Uma and Karlos could not have led me away from my mission. My mission is accomplished in the place that I am. Bomo was in my vicinity and yet I was preparing to scurry around a whole country to find him. All my answers were in my vicinity, all I needed to do was look. I have often accused people for coming in the way of my purpose and leading me astray. My purpose was always in my hands but I got so busy in distracting myself with other people's lack of purpose that I lost track of mine.

I could find Bomo because I stuck to my mission. When you break rules like Uma, you not only don't find Bomo, you also get lost. I wonder where Uma is. I hope she is safe! I hope she didn't get into trouble. I hope she is alive. I will find her tomorrow, just as I found Bomo today.

My future is shaped by today. It's not what I will do tomorrow that will shape my tomorrow. It's what I do today that will lead into tomorrow. Just like one can never quit smoking tomorrow, one cannot build a future in the future. My future is built today. And today, I choose to be bigger. I choose to do the right thing.

How come I KNOW all of this? How come I don't have questions anymore? Where did the questions go? How come I have all the answers now? How come I can see through people and circumstance?

Right now, I am happy I am here and I am happy Karlos is alive. I am happy that Uma had her way and is where she wants to be, for if she wanted to be here, she would be, like I am.

I am tired. I jumped from a parachute. Wow. I would do that again sometime, but my mom won't let me. I was scared of heights, but it was from that height that I could see the world. It was from above that I could understand myself and others. Down here I am involved but when I move to a higher ground I can see many perspectives clearly.

I didn't die in the jump. I guess I wasn't meant to, not yet. I have many lessons to learn and many lessons to teach. I am not done yet, and if Bomo would have his say I am sure he would say it's not my time to die. But I'm tired and I know it's time to sleep. And I will.

I am happy. Very happy.

CHAPTER 7 /

Finding Uma

I awoke that morning in a panic. I hated these stressful mornings. My life was moving at such a fast pace that sometimes I did not even know where I was or what I was doing. Sometimes I secretly wished that I would wake up at home, in my bed, and that this entire mission with Kurt would actually turn out to be a bad dream. But the mission with Kurt was more real than any bad dream I had ever had.

I had to find Uma. That was the first thought that crept into my head. As I sat up and looked around the cottage, I saw that Karlos was missing. I ran outside in panic and found him sitting on the grass, drinking a beer. The man was out of his mind, I thought.

"Its morning," I frowned accusatively at Karlos.

"No, its afternoon," he corrected me cheerfully.

I had obviously overslept. "I'm going back home," Karlos said, raising a toast to me. This was not the Karlos I knew. Maybe the near death experience had changed his priorities; I was no one to judge.

"We have to find Uma, Karlos," I told him with urgency in my voice.

But Karlos just sipped his beer nonchalantly. I decided to find Uma myself. "We have to get to the airport anyway," I reminded him. To get home he would have to get to the airport first. The man was being difficult. Even if he had decided to quit the assignment, he could at least be a gentleman and help. "No wonder he is single," I found myself muttering under my breath, like my mom.

Karlos was already two beers down. I went inside and packed all that I needed to. Just as I was stepping out, the young girl came running up, repeating the word Police. Damn, what was happening? I ran out to find Uma, accompanied by a policeman. "You know her?" he asked, as Uma ran towards me and hugged me.

"Yes, my friend," I said matching his broken english, holding Uma tight.

"You have her passport? Show me your passport," he questioned suspiciously.

"My passport is at airport with friend. We got lost. We have flight at 11 p.m.," I tried to explain in the tone that he would understand. I was telling the truth. I was not lying.

"Where your friend?" the policeman asked, still distrustful.

"At airport," I answered, totally in control and still holding Uma.

"Come with me," he commanded.

"Let's go Karlos." I signaled to him to come along.

Karlos got his bag. I turned back to see the fat woman and the young girl looking at us with fear in their eyes. They thought we were being arrested and would be sent to jail.

"All ok," I said to them and went up to give them a group hug. "Thank you for everything. You don't know but you have assisted us in a very expensive and dangerous mission. I will forever be indebted to you. Forget the money I paid to get here, meeting Bomo was worth all my life. Thank you very much." I knew they would not understand a word of what I was saying but that did not stop me from expressing my gratitude. They had earned it, and gratitude is an action, not a mere arrangement of words.

The woman said something in return, and I said, "God bless you too."

We walked in a line and moved through the trees about a kilometer uphill until we reached a road. It was a very narrow road, a mud road that had a police car parked on the side.

"Your friend at airport, eh?" the man asked with disbelief. He seemed delighted with the idea of arresting a bunch of illegal tourists. "I take you to airport; if your friend not there, I take you to jail."

The three of us sat in the car quietly hoping that Kurt would keep his word, for otherwise we were doomed. Uma put her head on my shoulder. "I'm sorry," she said.

"Never mind," I said. "At least you got us a free ride to the airport." And we all giggled.

"Did you meet Bomo, the keeper of the future?" Uma queried.

"Yes and how," I smiled.

"I missed it," Uma whined, slapping her hand on her knee.

"If anyone is hungry I have some mashed bananas and croissants," I said, and we all indulged in some much-needed laughter. The policeman observed us in the rear view mirror. We slept during the entire ride to the airport. This had turned out to be much easier than I had thought. I could see how it all had ended well, exactly the way it should have, except for Uma though.

I wondered where she had been all night. It was a shame that she did not meet Bomo. It was sad that Karlos was going home and Uma would be out of the program. I shivered at the thought that I was going to be alone for the next four days.

We arrived at the airport. Veni was there, as promised. She had our passports duly stamped and also our tickets. For a moment I wondered how Kurt was pulling off all the legal work with our visas. The policeman verified all our documents and then muttered something like, "These tourists are crazy."

Veni was delighted that we had all made it. While I inspected my passport, Karlos expressed his desire to quit. Veni made a few calls to confirm that Karlos would stay back to take the next flight to India.

I could see that he was happy. He was much happier than I had seen him through the entire trip. Maybe he had got what he wanted. Maybe this was as far as he wanted to go. Since Karlos was happy with his decision, I was happy for him. He seemed to have got his experience worth $25,000 .

"So you girls met with Bomo," Veni smiled.

"Yes," I said with a smile on my face, and I could swear I heard another yes behind me. It was Uma. She was smiling too.

No, she had not met Bomo. She had just confessed to me that she hadn't. And besides, I was the one with Bomo. She was lying. She had fled. I had told Kurt that. She was out all night while I was with Bomo. Oh my God, Uma was lying. I was furious.

Veni handed us our ticket and waved us goodbye.

I turned to give Uma a nasty stare. But right now my eagerness to see the next direction of my assignment was bigger than my contempt for Uma. I opened the envelope to find a ticket to Zurich. The instructions read:

You have come so far. Congratulations.

One of you will get the instructions at the next step.

Meet Louihi, the keeper of the past and take the message. Your next destination and task will be revealed to you. Follow the instructions. Good Luck.

Love and Prayers,

~ Kurt Rinck

We were flying economy to Zurich, all visas in place. I could not understand Kurt, and frankly right now I didn't understand anyone. I didn't understand Uma. I didn't understand that now there were just two people on the assignment; one fake and one real. My head was spinning with a dozen thoughts and I was having these mindless mental chatters about what others should do and how they should behave. I specialize in this mental verbal war and it always exhausts me.

I sat in my seat, fatigued. Uma had placed herself neatly in the window seat and was busy looking out onto nothing. We had not spoken a word since we got onto the flight. Honestly, I did not want to pick a row with Uma. I did not have enough courage to confront her and I would unknowingly pick a row with her in my mind for the rest of the journey.

The cabin lights were dimmed for takeoff and I decided to catch up on some rest. But hey, I had not written my journal. I got up, plucked out my journal from my bag, and tapped Uma's shoulder with it. "We've got to write," I said, forcing out a smile. Uma just nodded and continued to look out of the window.

I flipped through the pages I had already written and I began to write:

I am very upset with Uma. She cheated. She lied. And I don't like it. (I started to laugh suddenly. I could not believe I was writing a complaint in my journal. How petty! I thought)

*So Uma cheated and she is in the game. I did the right thing and I am in the game. The thing is that Uma cheated and she **thinks** she is in the game. What she does not know yet is that she is already out of the game. She will lead herself out eventually, for how can you achieve something when you don't understand it? Success is not an achievement; success is an understanding of achievement. The question here is how far will I remain in the game? I have to keep my focus on my learning else I will be out faster than Uma.*

But Uma was important; she led us to the airport after all. I could not have imagined moving past the old lady, or understanding how to get to the airport without directions and money. So Uma played her part in keeping me in the game. No one is useless and even the people who seem crooked have a purpose in our purpose.

I wonder if Karlos will go back home. I wonder what he learnt. He certainly looked happy. I wonder what changed for him. I guess when you earn a second chance to live, your life changes anyway. And sometimes, we don't get a second chance.

I wonder who Louihi is. I wonder what past she keeps. I thought my past was in my head so how could she keep it? I think I have kept my past safer in my heart and my head, than any Louihi could. I wonder what she would know about my past. I wonder if she knows those things too, those things that I had long past buried. I wonder if she keeps that too.

I don't know how I will survive Uma and how I will find Louihi. I guess Uma is not a threat, I make her a threat to me. We create people. We create them with our opinions about them. We can choose to be afraid of a cockroach too. Not that it is a threat, but we make it a threat and then react according to our perception.

How come I did not know all of this in the morning? How come I know now? There is some place this knowing comes from, and it seems to come when I write the journal. That's funny. It's the same me, but when I sit to write I seem to know.

I know now that I am happy. I am going to Zurich to meet Louihi and maybe I can check some other people's pasts too. Maybe I can check if my ex boyfriend really slept with my best friend. Heck, that would be madness. I need to let go of my past . . . but then why am I meeting Louihi? I guess in time I will find out.

CHAPTER 8 /

Louihi - Keeper of The Past

"Miss, straighten your seat, please!" the airhostess' voice pierced through my grogginess, waking me up to the previous day's disappointment.

I straightened my seat. "We are preparing to land," she said apologetically.

As I recalled the events of the previous night I felt tense. Veni had handed over charge of the next task to Uma. It had not bothered me when Veni had given the phone in my custody. However, it certainly bothered me that the next set of instructions was Uma's responsibility. If she could tamper with the truth about herself, she would certainly have no qualms about tampering with the instructions for the next task. Kurt's orders were 'Follow instructions' and now the instructions were in the hands of the girl who had cleverly broken the rules and gotten away with it.

Zurich was cold and we were lucky that this time we were not thrown off the plane in mid-air. Our bags had been packed and checked in for us, so I wondered if we had warm clothes. We had our passports and

I had guarded mine with my life for the entire journey. I hid it in the inside of my t-shirt and in case anyone asked to take it away from me again, I was planning to say that I had misplaced it.

As the airplane came to a halt, Uma opened the envelope and took out the instructions. She read:

Girls,

You will check into Hotel Continental. A cab will be waiting for you at the airport. You are forbidden from making any phone calls. (We had no money even if we wanted to.) If you are caught making a phone call, you will be out of the program immediately. The hotel stay is paid for. If money is needed, it will be sent to you.

Follow all instructions.

Meet Louihi, the keeper of the past, and get the message.

Love and Prayers,

~ Kurt Rinck

I was surprised that Kurt was being courteous this time around, though I sensed it was only the quiet before the storm.

The taxi was there as promised. We entered the Continental Hotel and checked in. "You are sharing the room," the receptionist said with a smile. "Your bags will be sent up to your room."

As Uma sat on the bed next to the door I quickly placed my purse on the one next to the window, as if to mark my territory. I wanted the bed by the window so that I could look at the skyline outside instead of staring at the walls inside. I hated this feeling of a cold war between us. Uma knew I was mad at her and her defenses were up, and knowing this only made me madder.

"What's the next instruction?" I asked. Uma opened the paper bag and took out another sheet.

"The next instruction is not to give you the instructions right now!" Uma said, raising one eyebrow and looking at me with a coy smile.

Ohoooo! This was getting sinister, I thought. I needed to get that sheet from her because I could clearly see she was lying.

Damn it, I had the girl sleeping on my shoulder last evening and now she had become my sworn enemy. What had happened? What had happened to me? Where had I lost my compassion and ability to connect? I could not understand! And my bad vibe was not helping. It was breaking me.

"So what do we do now?" I looked at her intensely, trying to judge her response.

"We do nothing till evening," Uma said, as she kept the brown package neatly in her bag and locked it. Then she calmly stepped into the shower.

Ok! Now this was a real test of my character. Uma was playing a game obviously to get me out of the program. I knew she had not met Bomo and the only way she would make it to the end was by getting me out of the way. What was I to do now? Actually what were my choices?

Kurt had said, "Follow instructions!" But now all the instructions were in Uma's hands.

I decided to keep a close watch on Uma. I was tired. I had not had a good night's sleep for days now. I had not slept on a proper bed for three nights. I decided to lie down and wait for Uma to come out of the shower. I would tackle this challenge one step at a time, I thought. I lay on my bed and before I knew it, I was fast asleep.

The human mind and body are a terrible combination if they are not in sync. If the mind keeps the body in consideration a balance is maintained. In the last few days my mind had neglected my body. I had grown spiritually and emotionally, but I had neglected myself physically. Lack of nutrition, rest, and sleep had taken a toll. Now, when I needed my body the most, it gave way. I fell asleep when I needed to be awake and watchful.

I woke up with a start. The phone by my bedside was ringing. "It's your wakeup call, Miss," the man at the other end said.

Damn, I had slept all afternoon and it was already 3.30 p.m. Uma's bed was still empty and untouched. Where was she? I began to worry a little. Where had she gone? I jumped out of bed and saw an envelope under the door. I pulled out the sheet of paper, which read:

> Reach Villa #8, Wayne Street at 5.30 p.m. sharp. Meet Louihi, the keeper of the past, and get the message.
>
> ~ Kurt Rinck.

There was a €20 note in it.

Where had Uma gone? I wondered if she had seen the message or whether it had been left only for me! I wondered if there had been money for her too. I wondered if she had taken more money and only left €20 for me. Grrrr. This feeling of doubt was driving me crazy. But whatever happened, I had to get to Wayne Street right away.

I flung open my bag. Uma's was nowhere in sight. Where did she stash her bag? Had she checked out? Oh my God, what was going on? I rushed through a shower and I sped downstairs with the map. Upon inquiring, I discovered that Wayne Street was on the other side of Zurich, near the mountains.

This uncertainty was killing me. Jumping off the aircraft and surviving in Genting Highlands was a much easier task. At least we were all together. We were a team. Now the team members had become opponents. How do you win in a situation like that? How do you trust anyone? How do you even live? I hated it, and I needed to resolve this before I lost my sanity.

The bus ride to Wayne Street was breathtaking. The snow-capped mountains in the distance, the snow covered houses, everything was even more beautiful than I had imagined. I had never seen snowfall before and I secretly wished that it would snow. It was so cold anyway, what harm would a little snow do? I did not have a camera and I was taking mental pictures of all the beauty that was whizzing past me. The snow gleamed in the faint sunlight and I loved the sight. It was clean and beautiful. The sky met with the mountains and exchanged notes on abundance and joy. The clouds were the same color as the snow only that the snow shone brighter. From cloud to snow is a beautiful journey and if one really cared to see, from mediocrity to greatness is the same beautiful journey.

The crowd thinned as we traveled further and further. Even amid this divine beauty I could not shake off the feeling that something evil was in store ahead. I wondered for a moment if Uma had gone to meet Louihi by herself and was just misleading me. I was apprehensive about this whole assignment but was ready to take responsibility for whatever happened to me. No matter how much anyone else tried to do things to me I could still control what happened to me. I wished Uma had not lied; I wanted back the sweet Uma I had briefly known.

The sun was setting and it was really, really cold. Kurt had packed a nice fur jacket for me, which I quite liked. It was my style. What I didn't like was having to do assignments at night. Why couldn't we just do them all in the daytime? I felt like a bat, sleeping in the day and working in the night. And the jet lag was not helping.

"Wayne Street," I heard the driver say as the bus came to a halt. I zipped up my jacket and hopped out. I had the note in my pocket and looked around for any signboard that could guide me to Villa #8.

There was no one in sight. This is one of the shocks an Indian has to deal with when abroad. We live in a country where we have to fight for even a foothold and here you are with no human beings in sight for miles. And then I saw it, a small board by the mud track that said Villa #8. It had an arrow pointing towards the river. I walked on the snowy, muddy track, and even from afar I could see that the villa was a beautiful house by the side of the river. This place was even more picturesque than Zurich. The walk to the villa seemed long in the icy cold weather as I trudged along the path. The sun had set a while ago and the entire street was beautifully lit up.

Unlike the other villas, Villa #8 had no name, just a number. There were a few cars parked outside and I gathered there were visitors. I rang the bell at the fence gate and faintly heard it ring indoors. The French windows were covered with thick curtains and I could not see inside. Smoke was rising from the chimney.

No one answered the door. I rang the doorbell again after having waited patiently for some time. I could hear the distinct ringing of the doorbell inside but no one seemed to come out. It was way past 5.30 p.m. and I was getting a little edgy. I inspected the door and saw that there was only a bolt on the wooden fence door, there was no lock. I turned open the bolt and walked inside. Another narrower snow-laden mud track led up to the house. The house was well lit. A heavy wooden door at the entrance to the house stood slightly ajar. I gathered there was no point in ringing the bell again and stretched out my hand to push the door open. As my hand touched the door, a cat shrieked and jumped out of the way. I shrieked louder than the cat as I barely stopped myself from falling backwards. Damn the cat! It was on the floor now, eyeing me warily, and I knew it was not happy. It purred with hostility and I decided to keep an eye on it as I pushed the door open.

The inside of the house was very dimly lit. The main door did not open into a living room but opened instead into a sort of waiting area. There were many doors that led out of the waiting area, and two wooden stairways, one going up and another going down.

I saw a dozen shoes by one of the doors. Maybe there was a religious ceremony going on inside, I thought. In my country it is customary to remove one's shoes outside when ceremonies or prayers are conducted. I sat down on a little chair to remove mine too.

The wooden staircase creaked and I heard footsteps coming up. It was Uma. "Where were you?" I was surprised that I was more concerned than mad.

"You are late!" she said in a Kurt-like tone.

Oh my God, this girl had turned around. She was not the same person I knew. I did not want to wage war with Uma. If I made Uma my agenda, we would both lose. She had the instructions after all and I had to find a way around her.

It's a difficult task finding your way around people who are giving you a hard time because they know they have the power to call the shots vis-à-vis your life, your decisions, and sometimes even your happiness. Right now the power was in the wrong hands. Uma had been dishonest. But she had been given control of this situation to the point that my destiny, my learning and my winning were literally in her hands. What do you do in a situation like that? What do you do when your exam paper lands in the hands of the moderator who has an axe to grind with you? What do you do when your promotion letter reaches the desk of the colleague who would find pleasure in having you fired? What do you do when you have to go to work every day knowing you are not appreciated or even remotely welcome? Well, I decided to lie low for a while. Fortunately, unlike other graver long-term situations, I knew this one would end in four days.

Before I knew it, another woman, short and bent over, came behind Uma. She must have been at least a hundred years old. She was wearing a black cape-like gown and the hood was pulled down. Her face had layers of wrinkles but somehow she looked stunningly radiant. I was shocked at how someone so old could look so beautiful. She had deep green eyes, and teeth that just hung in her mouth like chimes and swayed every now and then as she opened her mouth. I could only stare at her, thinking how beautiful she was. It was crazy to think of her in those terms but she was, in an inexplicable way, beautiful.

"You are late!" the woman barked accusatively, her teeth threatening to fall off. They were so loose that I could have actually put my finger in her mouth and pulled some of them out.

"Er, I'm sorry," I almost choked. I thought I had lost my voice. Was this Louihi? I asked myself.

"I am Loha," she said, as I tried to regain my composure. "I'm Louihi's sister. And Louihi does not like to be kept waiting." She raised an eyebrow in discontent.

I did not want to argue or justify my being late. "Let's go then," I said.

Uma took my arm and led me out of the house almost dragging me as she did.

"Wait!" Loha's voice thundered in the background. As I turned around I was surprised to see that her teeth were still intact. "I will come with you," she said lifting her cape and walking hurriedly in our direction. I did not know whether it would offend her if I lent her a hand.

Uma was still holding on to my arm and I was a little wary of her attitude. What did she know? Where was she taking me? By the look of it, Uma seemed ahead in the game for now. Uma took us through the back yard and pushed the little garden gate open. There was an open field ahead. Uma now tugged at my arm as Loha suddenly shouted, "Run before the gateway closes," and before we knew it the three of us began to run with Loha in the lead. That hundred-year-old bent over lady was giving us a heads up. Man, I began to run as fast as my feet could carry me and Loha was still about twenty feet ahead of me.

I could not see anything at all in the distance. It seemed that we were running towards nowhere. As we ran a few more meters, I could see a boulder formation; lots of gigantic boulders. I could have sworn that the boulders were not there when we started running. They had just not been there. Maybe my eyes were playing tricks on me. We could not possibly have run miles to have missed the sight of such large boulders. They were the size of a small hill, and I could see a distinct light between the gaps.

"Run," Loha screamed turning around. Now we were almost fifty meters away from a very distinct gap between two boulders, a sort of pathway, leading into the centre of the earth.

As we approached the boulders, I heard a loud rumbling sound as the earth shook beneath my feet. I almost lost my balance and fell. Uma caught my arm just in time. A few meters away from the gap I could see the boulders shift in formation, closing the gap.

"RRuuuuun," Loha shouted as she reached the rapidly narrowing opening. Oh my god. I was going to miss the opening. In two long strides Uma glided through the gap. I could see the boulders close in so rapidly now that I feared my body would be smashed between them. As I froze right at the entrance Loha pushed me inside with one powerful thrust and I heard a large crashing thud behind me.

There was darkness. Pitch darkness.

"Uma," I almost croaked.

"Shhhh," I heard her say and then her face lit up in the dark as she lit a match. We both looked at each other reassuringly and then looked around. I could see a torch edged into the wall but before we could walk towards it, the match died out. Uma lit another match and held it close to the mouth of the torch. With a roar the torch came alive, its large flame lighting up the interior of the cave-like boulders.

"Where is Loha?" I looked around.

"She missed the entrance," Uma spoke sternly. "Because of you!"

"Where is Louihi?" I asked, trying to change the topic. This was not the time to play the blame game. I needed to get to Louihi fast. I did not like the feeling of being caved in. I wanted to meet with Louihi and be out. Uma had led us here, so I gathered she knew where Louihi was.

"And how will we get out of here?" I asked, as I tried to heave the boulder that had just rolled shut.

"We will find a way out, just as we found the way in. Come," Uma said as she plucked out the torch from the wall, and we began to tread carefully on the boulders.

The boulders were huge and were piled one on top of the other. All I could see was a wall of very large stones with dark gaps between them. It was like a maze. How would anyone know which gap to go through? I soon got my answer; there was only one gap large enough for a person to go through. It had to be the one. Going through it seemed as though we were stepping down into the centre of the earth.

We continued walking down, stepping on the stones, sometimes squatting to squeeze through a gap. Uma would always stand away asking me to step down into the darkness first as though she was in control, calling the shots. I had to gather all my courage to step down into pitch darkness. The torch did not help because its light threw sinister shadows that freaked me out. In dealing with Uma's attitude, I was dealing with my own fears of moving forward, of taking the lead, of taking the first step into the unknown. I could remember the numerous times I had waited in queues and lost my turn because I did not want to be the first to speak up, to own up, to stand up! I could see how I had waited like Uma for someone to lead the way so I could ride on someone else's courage.

As I stepped into the darkness one more time, the torchlight revealed a very large opening. It was bound by tight boulders on all sides. There were two very distinct large openings with an unlit torch hanging between them.

Uma and I stared at each other trying to decipher what that meant. There were two openings and a second torch. Before I could ask Uma anything, she took the torch from my hand and moved forward, lighting the torch on the wall. We now had twice the light. She removed the torch and gave it in my hand.

"I go through this opening, you go through that," Uma said, pointing towards the opening to the left.

"What? We can't do that!" I protested. I was convinced that Uma was leading me into a death trap.

"I have the instructions," she said calmly. "We split forces here," she motioned.

"But where do we meet? Where are you going? Where is Louihi?"

Damn it, this girl was being so difficult. We were in this spooky, sinister place. The entrance had closed down on us. How would we get back? How would we meet again?

"I have the instructions," Uma repeated with authority. "We split here," she said as she began to move towards the entrance on the right. "We will meet outside." Before I could protest, Uma stepped down through the large gap. For a few moments I could hear her footsteps and I could see the flickering light of the torch from the gap. And then it disappeared.

I began to shiver with fright and decided to hurry down the gap on the left. Standing here would be no good. It is best to keep moving on when fear strikes. I knew the boulder was closed shut behind us so there was no point in going back. I had to meet Louihi, the keeper of the past, and the only possibility of meeting her was by moving forward.

I climbed down the gap and was surprised that the formation had turned very narrow and small. I had to almost bend my head so I would not bop it on the boulder above. Sometimes the gaps were like steps down and sometimes I had jump a few feet down. As I took a big jump down I saw a light flickering in the distance.

"Uma?" I whispered. Maybe our paths had crossed, I thought hopefully. Then I heard a chuckle. My body went numb and my blood froze in my veins. I did not know whether to run back towards nowhere or to step forward and join in the joke. With my heart racing, I stepped through the gap towards the light. I saw an old bent over lady. She looked quite similar to Loha. I squinted my eyes to look at her carefully. The old bent over woman chuckled again. She was dressed in a black cape just like Loha but she looked ugly. She was definately not Loha.

"You must be the same girl!" she said, looking at me with delight as though I was a prey that had walked into her den.

"Wh....," my voice disappeared mid-way as my teeth chattered.

"Are you the same girl?" she asked, pointing towards me and squinting her eyes as though trying to place me. "Ah," she said as her eyes lit up. "You are the same girl whose birth was mourned by her family," she chuckled.

Oh my freaking God. How did she know that? It is true that I was born into a family where a girl-child is unwelcome and almost considered inauspicious. But how did she know?

"Tsk, tsk. How you have secretly wished that you were a man!" she mocked. "It's a pity that you never made peace with your womanhood. You despised your womanhood so much that you became a man in every way that you could," she continued. "Look at you! A woman fighting to be the man she never was!" and the cruel old lady burst out into laughter threatening to put out my torch with her outburst.

That was such a mean thing to say, I thought, as tears welled up in my eyes. It was true that I was never given the respect I deserved because I was a woman. It was true that I wished I was born a man. It was true that I had lived my life in guilt for being a woman. As the old woman laughed, I felt tears roll down my eyes.

"Are you Louihi?" I asked her hesitatingly.

"Louihi is waiting for you," she said hurriedly. "Hurry before you are late." She walked out of the gap I had gotten in from.

I wiped my tears and continued down but I could not shake off the cloud of misery that now hung over me.

I took one more step down and I gasped. The same woman stood there again, holding a torch. She ignored me and continued on her way. Was it the same woman? Maybe not, this one had thicker eyebrows.

"Are you the same girl?" she quizzed exactly like the mean old lady who I had met above. "Are you the same girl who ran away from home when her grandfather died?" she laughed. "He died and left you alone to die too. You are the same girl, right?" she pointed her finger accusingly at me.

"Y...y...yes" I said, as a bucketful of tears rolled down my eyes. I was the closest to my grandfather. He was my pillar of strength. He was my world. He would tell me bedtime stories. He would share my laughter and would laugh away my tears. He kept my world safe. When he suddenly died one day, it shattered me. My world ended and I could not bear to be home anymore. Without him I was nothing. I had run away from home only to be brought back with a lot of shame and accusations. My grandfather's death had marked a lot of misery for me. I looked for my grandfather in every man I met, and that put an invisible burden on all my relationships.

"A...are you L...Louihi?" I asked her through my sobs. She obviously knew my past and so it must be her.

"Louihi is waiting for you, you poor miserable girl!" she laughed as she pointed towards the gap.

Where were these old women coming from? Who were they? How come they knew my past? I raised my torch towards the gap the old woman pointed to and without a question, I stepped into yet more darkness.

As I flashed my torch around I saw it was a bigger place. Another bent over lady, in a similar black cape, was walking into the distance almost getting through a gap.

"Louihi, wait!" I shouted as I finally found my voice.

The woman turned around. She looked similar to the other two old women, except that she was even uglier. I almost held my breath as I saw her. Her eyes were bulging, almost falling out, and her chin was almost hanging off her face. The torch shook dangerously in her trembling hand.

"Oh! You!" she said, as she stopped and raised the torch to look at me. "You must be the same girl," she said curiously. She began to walk towards me in short but hurried strides as though to attack me.

"You must be the same girl who slept with her boyfriend's best friend," she looked at me shaking her head accusatively. "What kind of horrible person does that?" She inspected my tear stricken face. "And to think that the poor man never found out," she laughed aloud and then stopped suddenly. "But you suppressed the shame and buried the guilt and strode on to con other men with your innocent charm," she said, raising her hand to slap me.

Defensively, I buried my face in my hands and sat down. I felt weak. Sleeping with Ron was a mistake. I was drunk. We all were drunk. I didn't know how it had happened. It was a mistake. I knew that Ron had the hots for me, and I had secretly liked him too. That Christmas eve while Chris was away, our feelings surfaced after half a dozen vodka shots. I was too drunk to resist Ron. It was just that one night, that one time, but I had slept with my boyfriend's best friend. I guess Ron never told Chris but we broke up shortly after that incident. It was true that I had lived with that guilt in all my relationships. And because I had cheated, I always suspected my men would cheat. Because I had broken Chris' trust, I could never trust any man I ever dated. I accused every man for the mistake I was never caught for.

"I'm sorry, Louihi," I mumbled an apology. I could not bear to even show her my face. She had brought to surface my worst and darkest secret. A secret that was killing me with shame. A secret that had already killed my ability to love and trust.

"Louihi is waiting for you," she said, pointing further down as she hurried towards the opening I got in from.

How many more of these women would I have to confront? I felt weak. I turned around and I saw my shadow behind me. My past would never leave me. It would follow me everywhere I went, just like my shadow. I had no strength to walk. I was shattered. How did this old woman know?

I picked myself up and staggered through the gap. Tears kept rolling down my cheeks and I was sobbing hysterically. If this was what all these women knew, I wondered what Louihi would say.

I came to a very large opening. The boulders had cleared for over a few feet. There were large boulders overhead and I could see that there was no beam holding them together. I shuddered. It seemed like a magical arrangement. I was convinced that with even as much as the sound of a sneeze, the boulders would dismantle and bury me down here. I stopped sobbing instantly. The opening surprisingly was filled with torches at intervals. The place was bathed in a faint orange light, and no one seemed to be there.

I wiped my tears to get a better look. Meeting Louihi, the keeper of the past, was turning out to be a nightmare. My soul was riddled with shame. I was convinced that she would kill me with my past.

"Louihi," I whispered, hoping she would not hear me. I was hoping she would be mad that I was late and send me back.

"I smell sinful blood," the voice that rang through the boulders. I could hear a deep rumble and felt tremors under my feet. And there she was. I did not have to ask if she was Louihi, she *was* Louihi.

There she was, emerging from a large gap, a very, very old woman. She was older than old. It was not really an old, shriveled face, it was sort of rotten, like a rotten vegetable. Her face and demeanor were just like that. One look at her sent shivers down my spine. She looked spooky, eerie, and evil.

"I smell sinful blood," Louihi said again.

It sure was mine. I felt sinful in every drop of my blood. I felt weak and shameful in every bone of my body. I had already met the other women before Louihi; they had done a great job in reminding me of my shortcomings and sins. They had selected those exact moments of my past, which had the capacity to destroy my very being. It had taken me a long time to get over the humility I had faced as a girl child. It took a long time for me to make peace with my grandfather's death and to take responsibility for my life. It had taken the longest time for me to forgive myself for sleeping with Ron and to move on with my belief in love. But, in a few short moments, the mean old women had broken me completely. There was nothing left for Louihi to break anymore.

Louihi beckoned me to come forward. I did so very hesitatingly. I was too scared to even sob. I choked down my sobs so as not to offend her. My cheeks were streaked with my dried tears and my mouth was dry.

Louihi came to the centre of the room and with one wave of a torch nearby she lit a devilish fire pit. Oh my God! Was Louihi going to throw me into this pit? Was this my redemption? I had obviously sinned, so was she going to burn me alive? My head spun as these thoughts ran through my head.

"What a shame," Louihi said, as she walked around the fire and came towards me. "What a shame you are!" she said, as she fixed her gaze on me. "Sit down," she motioned.

I sat down immediately. I had wanted to sit down. I had wanted to lie down. I needed to sleep and hoped this would all be a nightmare. I wanted to wake up in my house with my dogs by my side, reassuring me that I had had a bad dream. The good thing about nightmares is that they end when you wake up, but this moment in time was a nightmare that would keep me trapped in its grip for the rest of my life. I wanted to go home.

"Wait here," she said as she disappeared behind me. I stared blankly at the flames that had now become smaller and friendlier in the fire pit.

I wondered what message Louihi would give me. She obviously knew my past just as she held the past of the entire world. The other women seemed to be keepers of the past too.

In all my shock and shame I failed to see one thing; the old women who met me along the way had only brought up painful and shameful instances of my past. Everything they had said was loaded with trauma, pain, regret, shame, and guilt. But that was not ALL of my past. I had had a great time in my life too. There had been equal moments of happiness, joy, passion, and carefree abandon. There certainly were moments of achievement and power and glory, but they very cleverly, only brought out those issues which they knew would destroy my faith in hope and redemption. And they were right, because they did. They pulled me down so much that I now looked at my whole existence as a shame. I felt reduced to zero, to nothing, to nobody, like a person sentenced to death.

Attention is a funny thing. Whatever you direct your attention to, will become real for you. If you direct your attention to the past, it will become real in your reality today. My past had become real and I could feel it take control over me, in the way I felt, in the way my body became heavier, in the way my mind began to work and in the way my energy and rationality began to decline.

"And now," Louihi spoke from behind me, "let us look at who you really are. You can't hide from me. You can't run from me. You can't pretend I don't exist." She spoke in a shrill voice as her sinister face turned orange with the dancing flames.

"I am the keeper of your past, your sinful past!" she announced with pride, "And those!" she pointed through the gap to the women I had met earlier, "they collect your sins for me! That's how they remember you."

"You are capable of murder. You have so much negativity in you, it could destroy the world. You must be destroyed." She looked up at me.

I had seen many Louihi's in my life. Every person who would deliberately or unknowingly bring up my past to use against me was Louihi in action. Their intention was the same as hers, to break me, to pull me down, to gain control over me. I feel everyone has had points in their past that they are not proud of. And life moves on for everyone, offering many opportunities to make amends, and most of us do. I did. I had made amends for a lot of my wrongdoing. But when a painful past, even from two decades ago, is re-stimulated, it shuts down all rational thought, making us victims of our own mistakes and shortcomings .

"Look at your past," she mocked. I did not want to look at the past anymore. "You remember the time . . ." And Louihi spoke of one shameful memory after another, as I placed my hands over my ears. My head was reeling. Louihi came closer and took my hands off my ears with a jerk. Before Louihi could open her mouth and speak I pleaded, "No please. Please Louihi, I don't want to remember all of this! I don't want to remember any of it! No please, don't tell me. I don't want to remember." I began to cry. I knew Louihi would pull out more and more horrible things from the past and I knew that it would kill me.

Louihi looked at me fixedly and I felt like a victim waiting to be convicted. I was bent over, like her, holding both my knees with my hands, occasionally digging my face in my knees to cry. Louihi's persona was overbearing. She had reduced me to the size of an ant and I began to feel beat and pitiful. How could I not feel like a victim? Louihi knew my past, my darkest secrets, and referred to me as hateful and spiteful. She even suggested that I should be destroyed.

She knew nothing good about me. She did not know how I saved a stranger's life by risking my own. She did not seem to know how I had given up my savings to fund a school for orphans. She certainly did not know how I worked hard and served people. She obviously did not know my goodness, my greatness that co-existed with my fallacies. How could Louihi only keep my ugly past? Who kept my goodness? Where was my goodness? Where was my beautiful past?

I could not see this then, but Louihi had divided my life into the good and bad, the wrong and the right, the shame and the glory, the failures and the achievements, the lack and the abundant, the evil and the righteous. She had done it very cleverly and made only the former real. When we are under the spell of our sinful past, our behavior is born of insanity and madness. Anyone who is living in his sorrow laden past is evidence of that. It's frightening what living in it can do to our present life. I felt rotten. To live in the shameful past is rotten; I wanted to end it all. I was at my wits end and I wanted peace. I wanted to kill myself. Suddenly I felt there was no purpose in being alive. I hated my life and I hated myself.

"With the way you have lived your life, shuffling between ignorance and arrogance, to destroy is your only nature. There is no future for you, girl. Your future is cursed by your past, just like your present." Louihi's words stung my heart.

I wiped my tears. I had no answer but I wanted Louihi to stop.

"There is no hope for you," Louihi touched my cheek as she gazed at my tear stricken face. "Your past will never leave you. The more you live, the more other people will die. Save yourself. Save others," she said, pointing towards a large knife lying on a small boulder about ten feet to my left.

"Free yourself. There is no other way. Start a new life, and hopefully a better one." Louihi now goaded me on.

I couldn't believe Louihi was suggesting that I kill myself. She was suggesting that I take that large butcher knife and maybe slit my throat or wrist and bleed to death, and then start a new life all over again. Actually, I had contemplated killing myself many, many years ago when I ran away from home. I had almost staged my own killing in my head but had never had the courage to go through with it. Here was Louihi, encouraging me to take that step. She wanted me to free myself from all the misery that I had created and would continue to create for myself.

I got up. My body ached as I walked towards the boulder and picked up the large knife. Louihi was right. I had no business to live. I had hurt so many people based on the excuse that I was hurt. Yes, I was doing good to the world that did not know me, but the people around me were not happy. My mother was not happy, my father was not happy, no one was happy. A rage began to build in my heart. I needed to die.

I held the knife in my hand. With just one stroke, I could chop my hand and bleed to death. That would be my redemption. And maybe Louihi could throw me into the fire pit and make it easier. My hands were sweating and the knife was heavy. I raised my hand, the knife pointing towards my heart. Louihi was watching me carefully and moved her hand as though to say, "What are you waiting for?"

My hands were shaking and sweaty, the knife was threatening to fall down. I placed the knife on the floor and looked at Louihi as I wiped my forehead and then tried to wipe my hands on my pants. As I did that, I felt something in my pocket. I put my hand in my pocket and pulled out the ring Bomo had given me from the future.

It was the same ring from the same future I had seen and desired. My future was real. But I had such a horrible past. I felt terrible. But wait! I had seen a beautiful future, which meant I could choose. I could still choose. I could still change. I could still make it to the mountain house with the dogs, my baby girl and my gorgeous husband. There was hope. Louihi was lying. There WAS hope because I HAD SEEN the future. She wanted to me to kill myself because I had a horrible past, but I HAD SEEN the future. I had evidence of my future. There was hope, that despite all that I had been through and all that I had done, I could still make it to a better future.

I looked at Louihi. I quickly slipped the ring on my finger and turned around and began to run. I heard Louihi laugh, a laugh that filled the entire space. I ran towards the gap.

"STOP!" Louihi shouted and I froze in my tracks. "You can never run away from your past," she spoke, as I turned around and faced her.

"I am not running away from my past," I replied, looking straight into her eyes. "I cannot change anything that you keep. And maybe you can keep it with you forever because I can't anymore. I need to let go. I have a future waiting for me and I can't take my past along. There is no place for my past in the future that I saw, Louihi. You can keep my past. Take it away from me. I want to move forward. I want to move ahead. I want to be worthy and I want to be loved. I need to go back to my life, Louihi."

I was half expecting Louihi to attack me and hold me prisoner but I was surprised that she looked calm. "I can only keep your past on one condition!" Louihi said, as she approached me. "IF you don't repeat it! With every repeated action of cowardice you make me powerful. If you don't want me to meet you at every bend, reminding you of what you have done then leave me behind. Never return to who you were. Never repeat what you did!"

"I wont, Louihi," I almost sobbed. "You know I won't!" I spoke as though she could see my soul. I meant it and I knew that she would see it.

"GO! GO AWAY!" she roared. "Never set foot here. This place is sinful. I rot on your account. Every time you sin, I rot!!! Free me, GO AWAY!" She screamed so loud that the boulders shook and rumbled and trembled and small chips began to fall. Oh my god, Louihi needed to stop, we would be caved in.

"GO AWAY!" Louihi raised her hands as I ran for the gap which was now shaking as the boulders were caving in. I ran with all my might and just as I stepped out, the boulders shut behind me.

I stood trembling, out in the cold night. I looked behind and I could see the whole expanse of the boulders tightening and collapsing into the earth, being consumed by it. My legs were shaking as I tried to run towards the villa ahead.

I reached the front lawn and decided to run out. I did not want to wait for Uma, I just wanted to run as far as possible from Louihi. I would never ever live out of my past. I would never repeat it. As I ran out towards the garden my foot tripped over a garden hose and I fell flat into the snowy wet grass. A hand reached out to me and I shuddered. It was Loha who was holding my arm.

"That was a mighty fall," she said as she laughed and her teeth danced in her mouth.

I got up all wet and muddy from my fall.

"It seems you were running away from your past," she went on as her teeth clanged into each other.

"You met Louihi!" she looked delighted. "She keeps the past, your sinful past, and she keeps it well. She will bring it down on you and bury you, until you want to kill yourself."

"Louihi is very powerful. She can convince you to destroy yourself 'today', and not only that, she will make you do it." She spoke about Louihi with great respect. "I'm Loha. I am the lesser known sister," she spoke. She sure was a better sister, at least she looked kinder, and she was helpful.

"Come with me," Loha said leading me to the little bench in the garden where the same scary cat was sitting. "Go, Michael, go," she shooed and turned around as she literally pushed me down on the bench. It had a thin layer of ice on it but I guessed if Loha, the ageless lady, could sit on it then so could I.

"I am the keeper of your past, the one that holds goodness, glory, and greatness. I keep memories of your passion, your courage, your love, your divinity. And I have a great store of it. But it is Louihi who has the power. It is so easy to stride ahead with pride; if you build your connection with your success and achievements and goodness in the past but with an eye on the gory details that Louihi shows, I become meaningless. Whether you can see it or not, Louihi is inside you. Every time you look backwards with fear you can pull out your shame from decades ago and bring it to life in your present. When you do that you have no present and no future. If you must look back, look for me. Feed me. Remember me. I am your reality too. I am here to lead you to freedom. Louihi is caved in, she will keep you caved with her. I am free. I am waiting for you to take me higher. Feed me with the same greatness as you did on occasions before, if not more. Feed me with the same love as you did in the past, if not more, and you will experience freedom every day. Louihi is also a reality of your past, but make me bigger than her. Make your goodness greater than your sins. Make your divinity bigger than any past deviousness. Make me the bigger one," Loha pleaded.

"Please make me bigger than Louihi." Loha looked into my eyes and I understood. I understood everything. My past did not need to destroy me. What I do today will be in the past tomorrow. I cannot change the past that Louihi keeps but I can make up for it by my daily actions of divinity, today and everyday. I can make Loha, the keeper of my goodness more powerful than Louihi, the keeper of my sins. One day Louihi, by virtue of non-existence will have no power over my life anymore.

"I promise I will make you bigger than Louihi," I looked into Loha's eyes and she started to laugh with delight. I began to laugh too. I had cried so much in the past few hours that I was happy to laugh.

"I must go," I said, getting up. Loha kissed my hand and waved me good-bye.

I walked back on the muddy track and felt the return bus ticket in my pocket. I wondered if Uma would return soon, but knowing Louihi, she was not going to let her go without a fight.

The bus ride back to the hotel was magical.

I had evidence of my future in my hands and I had thrown away my past for Louihi to keep. With Loha's essence fresh in my mind, I began to remember every instance of goodness, of love, of joy, of happiness. I remembered my dogs and I smiled. I remembered how funny and loving my mother was and I smiled. I remembered the time I sang for a bunch of really old senior citizens and I smiled broader. I remembered the time I got the entrepreneur of the year award and I felt proud. I remembered the time a fan wrote to me about how my books saved his life . . . And there came an avalanche of all the good memories and I felt so powerful that I could have run for the presidential elections in America.

It was very early in the morning. Time flies when one meets the keepers of time. It was already 2 a.m. and I wondered if my watch was playing tricks on me. It was a cloudy night and it was cold. But my mood was set. I was happy to get back to the hotel but there was still no sign of Uma. I hoped that Louihi would be kind to her and I hoped that she would survive her past. She was a good kid after all and I remembered all the good times that I had spent with her in the last few days. I remembered her courage and I remembered her innocence. I remembered how daringly she had jumped off the jet plane, and I smiled.

> *I am still upset with Uma. I did not like it when Uma was given all the instructions. The power was in the wrong hands....Ummmm..... Actually, power is in everyone's hands. We choose to let it go when we don't use it. How can it be that Uma has power and I don't? I have power over the decisions I make. I have power over the choices I make, and that's about all the power anyone needs.*

As I sat on my bed I realized how tired I was. I felt very light though. I had literally left my past behind. I was eager to write in my journal; I secretly looked forward to the end of the day so I could see it better.

Just because Kurt gave Uma the instructions it did not make her powerful. What I do with those instructions is what makes me powerful. No one can intimidate you if you can choose and decide for yourself. And everyone can do that even if they say they can't; that in itself is a choice they are making..

I thought I had buried all my past and moved on. I had tried building a future on my buried past. I had not succeeded in building a happy present let alone a successful future. You can't bury guilt and forget about it. You know where you buried it, and as long as you know it, it's there.

I can let go of my past if I learn from it and don't repeat it. I guess I was so ashamed and guilty of all the bad things I did that, in that charade of feeling bad I never learnt from it. I never questioned myself like the old ladies did; I just hid from my own wrongdoings.

I have let go of Louihi and I feel very happy. I feel happier than yesterday, and I know that this happiness is for real. No one can take it from me. There is no one who can put me down again. Loha will be the guardian of my past and that makes me happy.

I KNOW that a beautiful life lies ahead of me. I know I am beginning to discover a happiness within me. A happiness that needs no reason to exist. I feel happy for no reason in particular. And I love this feeling. I have never felt this way before. Somehow, the more I know myself, the more I leap forward and meet the keepers of time, the happier I become.

I can't wait for tomorrow. I know today has been a day well lived and I know everyday of my life will be too.

I smiled with joy as I put back my journal on the table. A folded note caught my eye. I opened it. It was a note from Kurt:

Priya

You will leave tomorrow for the Deborence Forest. You will meet Jade, the Keeper of the present. Take the message and get to the airport on 16th January for your flight at 10 p.m. Your tickets will be at the airport.

Love and Prayers,

~ Kurt Rinck

CHAPTER 9 /

The Deborence Forest

I slept like a log. If anyone was freed of the hold their past had on their life, they would sleep like me, like a log. When I woke up I did so with a smile. I was well-rested and there was nothing to do for the day. It was already past noon and I was in a beautiful country. I had no money to buy anything but then experience comes for free. And I had had more than my share of that in the last few days.

I would leave for the Deborence forest in about three hours and I decided to take my time getting ready. I showered lazily and packed my bag which was very tastefully filled by whoever had packed it for me.

I stepped out ahead of time and flipped through some Swiss magazines in the lounge. When it was time, I proceeded to check out.

The receptionist was polite and extremely pretty. She could run for Miss Switzerland if she chose to, I thought, but right now she was serving me with unimaginable hospitality. I could see that her presence certainly added to the guest loyalty program of the hotel.

"Your stay has been paid for," she announced much to my relief. Kurt sure kept his word.

"How can I get to the Deborence forest?" I asked her while she was filling out the forms. She looked up at me in horror, as though she had seen a ghost.

"Wh . . . where do you want to go?" she asked, trying to stay composed.

"The Deborence forest," I said, a little taken aback myself.

"No one goes there, Miss. No one has ever gone there. There is no access to the forest," she spoke with alarm and then began to look around as though worried that someone might have overheard.

"But I need to get there," I spoke with urgency. "Do you know anyone who can get me there?" I was now panicking. I had the whole day to myself. If only I had known that the place was tricky I would have left earlier. Damn! I should have done some research.

"No one who has gone into the Deborence forest has ever come back Miss. No one comes back alive. Can I call you a taxi for the airport?" she asked, hoping I would just take the taxi and leave the hotel.

"Can I leave my bags here? I'm going to find out about the forest. Maybe I can collect them later or tomorrow." I was not going back without meeting Jade in the forest. Whether anyone had ever come back from it or not, Kurt had given me the assignment and I had to do it. Only this time, I had no teammates, not even the mean ones.

"It would cost you €10 a day," she said, hoping the cost would deter me.

"That's fine," I replied as I signed the paper not knowing how I would pay for it later. The money was not a problem to worry about right now, finding Jade was. Often we start paying attention to the 'urgent' problem at hand and miss handling the 'important' ones that shape our lives. I decided to go out and look for someone who could help me with the Deborence forest.

I walked out into the street. It was a cloudy, chilly day. A taxi stood at the door expecting me to hop in. I knocked at the window and a large, elderly man in a chauffeur's uniform rolled the window down.

"Can you tell me how to get to the Deborence forest?" I asked him hesitatingly.

The man looked amused. "I can tell you how to get there, but I can't tell you how to get out," he laughed. "Everyone knows where the Deborence forest is, it's not a secret. And everyone knows that anyone who has set foot into it has never come out."

He eyed me cautiously. "Has someone cast a spell on you, lassie?"

"No, but I have to go there and meet Jade, the keeper of the present. Do you know someone who can help me?" I asked hopefully. The man certainly knew something because the minute I took the name Jade, his face tightened and he looked around suspiciously to see if anyone had heard us talking. This whole secretive attitude first on part of the receptionist and now on part of the chauffeur was killing me.

"Get in the car," he said as he started the engine.

I jumped in the car without any hesitation. The man drove in silence for a few miles, glancing continuously in the rearview mirror. I was beginning to get nervous..

"I'm Smith," he finally broke the silence after driving a few miles.

"Where are we going?" I asked, "And um, I'm Priya. I am from India and I need to find Jade, please." I almost pleaded.

"I'm taking you to Vicky. He will talk to you. No one speaks of Jade. Jade is the spirit of the forest. He is not a person, he does not exist, and he is not real. Jade is evil. He is a curse. You will never return if you lay your foot in that forest. Vicky will tell you. Someone has cast a spell on you," he spoke looking worried and uncomfortable.

We drove a few miles down hill and he pulled up near a rundown cottage. "Wait here," he said, as he got out of the car and disappeared into the bushes, which hid the cottage behind it.

Now I was beginning to get scared. I was scared of ghosts and spirits. I mean, if Jade was not a human form then how would I communicate with him? And what if I never returned? Maybe I could draw a map. Maybe I could carry some bread and throw it along the way to map my path. Maybe I could mark the trees so I didn't forget the way. I needed to do something, somehow, anyhow. This was my last assignment and I had to finish it. I had to get the message from Jade. Even if Jade was God I had to get it. There was no way I was going to back off. If Louihi could not kill me then I figured I had the courage to take on Jade.

The chauffeur came out with a middle-aged man. He was tall and heavy built, with average looks. His big moustache hid his thin lips. He walked out still buttoning up his coat; he had obviously not been expecting visitors.

"I'm Vicky," the man said, stretching out his gigantic hand. He spoke with a very distinct accent and smelt heavily of tobacco.

"You want to go to Deborence? You want to meet Jade?" He tapped his head and said, "Are you nuts? No one has come out alive from Deborence!"

Now this whole theory had begun to sound outrageous. I had heard it too many times already. But I had survived Bomo and Louihi, hadn't I? I was determined to go on.

"Will you show me the way?" I asked Vicky. My unexpected question took him by surprise. I knew he was prepared with a bagful of stories but I bypassed them all and asked him directly, "Are you in or out?"

The two men spoke something in French. I wanted to get out of the car and tell them that I was going to find a way to get there with or without them but before my hand reached the handle of the door Vicky leaned in at my window and looked me directly in the eye. "I will take you. But your life is your responsibility. I am telling you again . . ." Before he could complete his sentence I said, "No one has ever come back. I know. But I will."

Vicky disappeared inside the cottage. The chauffeur, Smith, stood near the car, shifting uncomfortably from one foot to the other.

In a few minutes Vicky came out with a big leather bag. He had two large sticks that looked like oars. He threw the leather bag on the back seat of the car and began to tie the sticks on the roof of the car. I turned to inspect the bag. It seemed to be made of animal skin, deer I guessed, by the color of the fur on it. I heard Vicky say something to Smith and then he got into the car and we drove off.

"What about him?" I asked, watching Smith walking towards the cottage.

"He will go home, I will take you," Vicky said as he lit a cigarette and stepped on the accelerator.

We drove past the city and onto a lonely highway. It was turning dark and I was beginning to have a bad feeling about this whole adventure.

Until now everyone had told me about how Deborence had no access, how anyone who went into the forest never returned, and how Jade, the keeper of the present was not a person but the spirit of the forest. Everyone had told me all the scary stuff, and yet I was determined to get there, meet Jade and return home. But now that Vicky had packed his bags and was taking me to Deborence, the reality of it all began to seep in.

At this moment, I wished I was not going on this assignment by myself; Karlos would have been some moral support, and even Uma with her manipulative ways would have been welcome. Suddenly I felt alone, very alone. I was about to venture upon a supposedly dangerous task and I was alone. Maybe I should go back. Maybe this was my only chance. How did the $25,000 matter anymore? It would not come back whether I finished the assignment or not. If I turned back I would be alive but if I ventured into the forest today, then maybe I would never return.

As the fear welled, so did my faith in Kurt. Why did Kurt want me to go and meet Jade in a forest from which no one returned? Either Kurt was betting on my inability to make it into the forest or he believed in my ability to create history by getting in and finding my way out. What did Kurt see in me? I could only find out by moving forward.

We drove the entire way in silence. The night grew darker and stars began to spread themselves out in the clear sky. A thin curved moon cast its light on the trees, throwing long and dense shadows on the road. The headlights cut through the darkness and Vicky slowed down, trying to locate a place for us to get in.

The fir trees on the side of the road were very tall, covering the forest like a huge umbrella. They were at least a hundred feet tall. The whole forest looked black with a hint of silver; the silver fir and the leftover snow gleamed in the faint moonlight. Vicky pulled over and stopped the car, the headlights still on. "Here we are," he said looking at me.

"This is the forest, Deborence. This is where Jade lives. No one has ever seen him, so I do not know how to describe him to you. All I wish is that you know what you are doing and that you will come back. If you have changed your mind, it won't make you less in my eyes, I will take you back," Vicky spoke slowly and deliberately, watching for any shift in intention.

"Aren't you coming into the forest?" I queried, eyeing his leather bag. I knew he had put two oars on the roof.

"I know that no one comes back, lady. And I know I am going back home. It just breaks my heart to leave you here," he said, looking at me persuasively.

I had expected Vicky to come along. That's what I thought he had meant when he said, 'I will take you there.' I really wished he would. I did not want to go alone. Not tonight.

"In Deborence, there is only one time of the day, the night. The sunlight is too feeble to penetrate through the trees. I would not even dare to go in the day, because the light feeds fears that the darkness conceals. If you were to see the eeriness of the forest in the light, you would never dare to step into it." Vicky was now puffing on his freshly lit cigarette.

Vicky was feeding my fears and he needed to stop. I was scared. I was determined but I was afraid. I needed some advice about the way and the path ahead. "Vicky, tell me something about Deborence," I said fearfully.

"According to the myth about Deborence, there is a lake in the forest, a still lake that is said to be connected with the centre of the earth. The myth says that the lake holds in it three worlds; the world of the land, the world of the water, and the world of the air," Vicky spoke nervously chewing on the butt of his cigarette.

"Jade is said to live on the other side of the lake. How far deep inside, I don't know. Frankly I don't know anything except the stories I have heard. And if you ever come out, I would want to know the story from you," Vicky said in a faint hope that I would survive to tell.

"Can you leave the car here, Vicky?" I asked. "You could leave the headlights on pointing towards the forest, that way I will have a point of light for direction when I am on the way out." My mind was working fast.

"Maybe you could leave the blinkers on, that would save on energy," I further added. "Without any reference it would be difficult to find my way out," I went on, playing on Vicky's emotions.

"You want me to wait here all night? And what if you don't come out tonight?" Vicky sounded alarmed at his involvement.

"Then you can leave me here and go back. I can't expect you to wait here forever, but maybe . . . you could wait here tonight, because no matter what happens in there with Jade, I am going to come back. I am going to live to tell the tale." I made a promise I knew I may never keep.

I had put Vicky in a fix.

"I will stay as long as the energy stays," he said, pointing to his fuel tank gauge. Thankfully it was three quarters full. That would give me a whole night to get to Jade, the keeper of the present, take the message and come back, or be consumed by the forest forever.

CHAPTER 10 /

JADE -
Keeper of The Present

Vicky got out of the car and opened my door. He flung the leather bag over his broad shoulder and brought me out of the car as though he was preparing me for battle. He gave me one oar. "This oar could serve as a weapon too. This is all I have in case you need to protect yourself. Though the stories say that the forest is a dead forest with no life, this is just in case of need," he pointed to the sharp edge of the oar.

"You are too pretty to never return. I feel sad to leave you here," Vicky said, giving me a hug. "I will be here till the fuel lasts." He hesitated for a few seconds before adding, "Please return." If he spoke any longer I would certainly change my mind and jump into the car and run home. I had to stay focused on my task. Now that Vicky was bidding me goodbye, his repeated advice to stay away from going into the forest seemed extremely tempting. I wanted to turn back and run.

But resistance has always given me power, whereas compliance has made me weak. I needed to trust my instinct. I needed to trust Kurt. There must be something here, there must be a reason and a lesson in this. Though my gait was hesitant, I turned around and walked across to the muddy grass that marked the beginning of the forest.

The trees ahead of me were gigantic. It was so cold that I feared I would freeze and die despite the thermals and fur coat I was wearing. I didn't dare to turn back and look at Vicky. There was no turning back.

As I took a step further, the headlights of the car went out and my heart sank into my feet. What had happened to Vicky? I wanted to turn around and run, I wanted to run for my life, but I held my ground. When terror strikes, don't run around like a headless chicken; hold your ground. I stood still, breathing so heavily that my lungs could explode and as the darkness settled in I could see yellow blinker lights come on and off. Vicky had turned off the headlights to help me adjust to the dark, and had turned on the blinkers to save energy.

There seemed no way into the forest. The trees were so dense it was almost like a wall of thickly woven bushes and parasite shrubs that grew on the majestic firs, spruces and larches. I stood about one foot away from the wall and the smell of a green world, sweet and mystical, filled my nostrils. It was an intoxicating smell, a smell that could enchant and cast a spell forever.

I took the oar and pushed it into the wall of the tightly guarded bush and tried to hack a hole in it. It worked. I squeezed into the bush and landed onto the other side, a further knit of wild green growth, tight and dark. Behind me I could see nothing except the blinking lights in the darkness beyond the bush. My idea had worked.

I had to grope my way into the forest to walk. At times I did not know what I was touching. I could faintly see three to four feet ahead of me. Strange looking bark surrounded me on all sides. I felt imprisoned between the trees. If I stood there long enough, I felt the creepers would grow on me, holding me prisoner. I shuddered and walked through the little gaps that I could see between the bark and the bushes, and the creepers and the loose-hanging vines. Everything I touched was ice cold. Sometimes when I touched a creeper it would withdraw, pulling me along with its hold. I lost my balance twice and was engulfed by the undergrowth. I had to fight the branches and the tall blades of grass and the thicket of roots to stand up again and take another step.

I could still see the on and off of a distinct yellow light from where I had reached. I knew that a few more feet into the forest and I would lose all connection whatsoever with the lights, with Vicky, with the whole world.

I held on tightly to the oar that Vicky had given me. He did not give me a flashlight even though I had asked for it. "The light will scare you more than the dark. If the forest was meant to be in the light, it would be. Some things are best conquered in their territory," he had said. "People often died of what they saw in the light and lived because of what they did not see in the dark"

I shuddered. Even if Vicky had given me a flashlight, I would not have dared to turn it on. I did not want to see what nature did not want to show me. I walked on. When I looked back one last time and as expected, a vast stretch of darkness lay behind me.

The forest was awfully quiet and that gave me the shivers. There was no sound of any insects or animals and not even the wind. The only sounds that I could hear were my footsteps, the tapping of the oar on the undergrowth, and my breath. The forest was so silent that I could almost hear my thoughts. It seemed like a 'dead' forest. The only life that apparently existed was the wild green.

As I took a few steps further I began to feel warmer, or maybe it was just my imagination. Maybe the heavy trudging was building up the heat under all the warm clothes I wore. I decided to walk on regardless.

A short while later I found myself next to a tight thicket of trees. The fir trees were over a hundred feet tall. I saw no sky, no stars, no moon, just darkness everywhere—overhead, below, all around. And now in front of me was a tight fence of closely-knit trees. There was no way I was going to pass through them with the weight I had on me. I tried to heave myself through the slight gap between the two trees but it was impossible. I walked a few meters to the left and few meters to the right looking for another way to enter but to no avail. It was as though the forest was a fortress; you could come so far but now to get further you had to be really determined.

I knew that if I got rid of my jacket and my sweater, I would be able to make it to the other side. I also knew that without my jacket or the sweater I would not survive. I was thinking fast.

I removed my jacket and sweater carefully and I waited to adjust to the cold. I was surprised I did not feel cold. It was rather warm. It was not my imagination, it really was warm. I could feel the warmth in my breath but I was not taking any chances. I held my coat and stretched my hand through the gap between the two trees to drop it on the other side so I could retrieve it as I entered. As I was about to drop the coat on the other side, I felt something jerk it out of my hand.

My heart missed a beat and a sharp pain in my chest threatened to kill me. Someone had snatched the coat from my hand on the other side of the tree wall. I wanted to run back. I wanted to run back till I could see the blinkers, follow the lights and get back to the car. I was on a lonely mission . . . no, I was on Kurt's mission . . . or was I on my mission? I could not believe that halfway into the forest and almost at the end of my seven-day journey I was confused about why I was here. I could not think clearly. Why was I doing this to myself? Why had I trekked into a land of no return? Why was I playing with my life? What would this be worth? Why was I doing this for Kurt? Or was it to justify the money I paid for the seminar? At this point I began to question the purpose of my journey! I have asked myself the right question at the wrong time all my life. After I got engaged, I began to question if I really wanted to get married. After I finished my master's degree, I began to question if this was the career I really wanted to pursue in my life! After I got money and fame, I began to question if this was what I really wanted. I had asked the right question for sure, but after coming this far even if I realized that I was on the wrong track, the journey back would be far more painful than the journey that got me there. To break up my engagement was more painful than getting engaged. To accept that I was lonely was more painful than having the money and glory. To realize that I was heading for the wrong career was far more painful than the two years spent in study. And here I was, questioning myself again.

As I gathered the courage to heave myself through the gap again, I realized that I would never have known what was right for me if I had not immersed myself in the experience. How would I know if the man was right for me if I didn't spend time with him? How would I know what I was meant for if I didn't complete the degree first? How would I know that there was more to life than money and fame if I had not gotten it first? The real test of a decision is found at the end of the journey, and life is beautiful because every journey that ends marks the beginning of a new one, a new purposeful one. It is then that you understand the path and the purpose of reaching there. I came to the forest because I had an assignment, but I stepped into the forest because I had a purpose. What was that purpose? I guess I would find out on the other side.

I peeped into the gap and saw a light shining like a twinkling star on the other side. Someone was there. Maybe it was Jade. The light gleamed again, sort of like a patrol light that comes and goes. If Jade was on the other side, I had to meet him.

Maybe he would kill me. Maybe he would trap me. What worse could he do? Or maybe he would give me the message. I had come so far. It would be insane to return now. And I knew if I returned now, I would be haunted for the rest of my life. I would live the rest of my life regretting not having completed my task and getting the message from Jade. I was going to confront it, him, or whoever it was, get my message and be on my way home.

I pressed the oar through the gap, first put one leg through, and then heaved my body on the other side, crashing through the dense thicket.

As my eyes took in the scene before me, my jaw fell open. Ahead of me lay a stunningly beautiful lake with water so still it held the whole sky within it. No, it seemed as though it held the whole universe in it. The reflection of the curved moon shone in it. It was the same light that I had seen from the gap. The lake lay in the centre of a magical clearing a few miles in diameter, dividing the forest into two halves, one where I stood and one across the lake. The solid wall of trees stood all around, guarding it.

My coat lay on my side. I looked around; there was no one in sight. It was an expansive clearing and it was really warm here. I removed another layer of thermals. It was heavy to carry my coat and sweater and thermals along. I decided to place them next to the gap to mark my exit point before walking towards the lake.

It was not just beautiful, it was enchanting. There was no sign of life, no creepy crawlies, no insects, no bugs, no flies, nothing except for the stillness of the trees, the sky and the lake. As I neared the lake I thought I saw a dark form, which on closer inspection turned out to be an overturned boat. Vicky was right; there was a lake and I was going to need an oar. If there was a boat then there would certainly be an inhabitant. I was on the right track. Someone was here for sure ... Jade?

On the far side of the lake was an expansive wall of trees, just like the one behind me. I inspected the boat. It was dry, indicating that it had not been used recently.

I have had spells of loneliness in my life, but right now, standing in the middle of the forest, I realized that in fact all my life I had so much life around me, so much energy around me, that it was impossible for me to be lonely. Because of my attitude and inability to deal with my own world, I had distanced myself from people who loved and cared for me, and I had created a lonely life for myself. Now, in this forest, with no sign of life whatsoever, I understood what loneliness was. For the first time in my life I began to appreciate friends and family whom I had so conveniently ignored all along.

Right now I was on my own and I had to count on my own judgment to keep me safe. I had to get to the other side of the lake as Vicky had said. I used all my strength to overturn the boat. It made the loudest splash as it hit the water. Oh dear lord! The splash echoed through the trees and I shivered. The whole forest had acknowledged my presence and I stood still, trembling, half expecting to be attacked by the spirits of the forest. The echo continued as I held tightly on to the edge of the boat. As the water touched my feet, the ground disappeared and I almost fell into the pit that had freshly formed under my foot. In the faint moonlight I saw that every drop of water was consuming the ground as it rocked and ebbed.

I remembered Vicky's words: "The lake is connected with the centre of the earth and holds the three worlds in it—the earth, the water, and the air."

I skipped and jumped to avoid any contact with the water and in one push I jumped into the boat holding on tightly to the oar.

With one big thrust of the oar the boat began to glide on the water that was now too rocky for my comfort. I tried to keep my balance as the boat moved smoothly on the water. I was not even rowing and yet the boat seemed to be moving of its own volition. I tried to take control and pushed my oar into the water to get a hold on the ground but there was none. I did not dare to look down and kept my eye on the other side of the lake where Jade lived.

In all this fright and uncertainty about Jade and what would happen I realized that this person, or spirit, was a lot like me. He lived in a well-guarded world, private and lifeless, just like mine. In a funny way I could relate to him. And because I could relate to him, it lessened my fear of him. I guess when we find a point of relation to people, no matter how difficult they may seem, we get connected. And when you can connect with people, you can win them over.

The boat glided and reached the end of the lake. It stopped with a jolt almost tossing me out. I jumped out and landed on the grass bank.

Now where was this darned Jade? I decided to call out to this 'Jade' person or spirit. If whoever it was really lived on this side of the forest, then there was no point looking for him anymore. He would know of my arrival by now by the ruckus I had made, and if he was smart he would certainly be expecting me.

"Jade!" I called out as though he was close by, and waited for a response, half expecting a ghost-like figure to emerge. There was none. "Jade!" I shouted a little louder. There was still no response. "Jade!" I shouted even louder this time and the echo bounced in every direction. And finally as the last jade bounced off, I heard a knock. Not a knock but a thud, repeated thuds, like continuous hammering against a glass door. The thuds were coming from behind the tall bush just ahead on my right.

I have a weak heart; a sound like this has the capacity to send me straight into the ICU. Right now, to get to the emergency room of a hospital, I would have to jump on the drifting boat, cross the bottomless lake, make my way through the thin gap between the trees, find my way between the wild and ever tightening trees to spot the blinking lights and get to Vicky's car. The ICU was far away in another world and in this moment all I could do was ignore my heart and find Jade.

The thuds continued. What kind of language was this? Like the Morse code? And in a forest like this it would need a very thick heavy object to make a thud sound like that! Maybe Jade was a spirit and only communicated in thuds this manner. I was sorely in need of advice but whom could I turn to? And maybe it was too late to get advice. This is the kind of situation I want to turn around and ask someone, "What should I do now?" But every time I have asked this question, I have received the wrong answer, if not a big lecture. If I would have asked my mother this question, she would have told me how it was wrong for me to be here in the first place and how irresponsible I generally am and lord knows what direction her answer would take. If I would have asked this question to Vicky, he would have asked me to run back. If I would have asked Kurt this question, he would have told me that I had no right to ask questions. But I guess the real answer to any question lies in moving on. "What should I do now?" The only option was to move on, to explore and discover for myself what lay ahead.

I gathered courage and took a step closer to the bush. I heard more thudding behind me. And as I spun around, I heard all around, thudding and thumping echoing violently from every direction. The thumping grew so loud and the echo so deafening that I placed my hands on my ears and shouted, "STOP!! STOP IT!!! JUST STOP IT!!!" And as if by magic, a silence fell over the whole forest. A very sinister silence. This Jade entity was mad, I thought. Why was he making so much noise? Couldn't he see me? Was he out of his mind?

I walked up slowly towards the bush, determined to confront Jade or at least to see what was on the other side, causing all this noise. The moonlight was faint but its reflection from the lake was lighting up the otherwise dark clearing. I walked cautiously on the other side and as I opened up the branches I died a thousand deaths. I stood there lifeless, as a man with big bulging eyes, sunken face, and skeletal form peered at me. He seemed to be leaning against something invisible, maybe glass, and thumping on it. There was nothing around him and yet he thumped on it. I stared at him in disbelief as he turned around and thumped all over, all around.

Jade! Was this Jade? He was human after all! But what was he doing thumping in thin air? I looked closer and I saw that he was inside a clear glass-like wall, sort of trapped from all sides. Why was Jade trapped? I walked cautiously towards him.

When I was about three feet away from him, he spoke in a faint muffled voice, "Help me."

"Help me," he pleaded again, as I gazed in fascination at his big, bulging eyes.

I was confused. Vicky had said that Jade would trap me forever but here was Jade trapped himself begging me to free him. I stretched my hand to touch the glass and suddenly the whole forest came alive with the thumping. I froze. How many Jades were there? What was going on?

I ran to the other side of the bush and I saw another man, another form. I saw more men, almost a dozen men, trapped in this glass structure. I ran towards them and suddenly they stopped. They had got my attention.

"Who are you? Are you Jade?" I asked the man with the bulging eyes "Why are you in here?" I questioned, "And who are they?" I said, pointing towards the dozen men who stood similarly in all directions. In one breath I had asked so many questions.

"I am not Jade," the man shivered as his voice muffled out of the glass trap. "I am trapped. I am trapped, just like everyone else is," he said, looking around. "I am trapped in time."

"Trapped in time?" I could see nothing there but as I stretched out my hand I could feel an icy cold structure.

This is a time trap, I thought. These were all the people who had come into the forest and never returned... because they were trapped in time.

"How long have you been here?" I asked him.

"Forever," he said.

"And you will be here too," a man spoke from behind him, "because Jade will not let you go."

"Wh . . . Why won't Jade let me go?" I asked with a hint of panic.

"Because I am the keeper of the present," a voice, a thick and loud voice, spoke from behind me.

I spun around but no one was there.

"Where are you, Jade?" I questioned and I was surprised at my own fearlessness.

"I am here," the voice spoke, as a little boy of maybe five or seven emerged in front of me. He had big black eyes, fair baby-like skin and the most innocent smile in the whole world.

"Y . . . you are Jade?" I was surprised. I had expected an old, shriveled, mean person if not an unholy spirit. After all, how was this little innocent boy capable of putting a dozen overgrown men ruthlessly in a time trap?

"Yes, I am Jade," the boy spoke, delighted at my recognition. As he spoke his form changed and he turned into a man, a well built man majestically attired like the one who rides a chariot for the kings. I was startled. I almost jumped backwards. Before I could react to this transition from boy to man, Jade had quickly changed form and turned into a man covered with wounds oozing blood. I was stunned. Jade obviously had magical powers. He could turn himself into any form he wanted. I shivered.

"Who are you?" I squinted, as Jade showed off his might by rapidly changing forms from boy to man to girl to woman, and from ugly to beautiful to powerful to defeated.

"Who are you?" I asked, as an old man now stood in front of me. He was an old wizard-like man. He had a long white beard and long white hair. He wore a silver robe and looked like a wise old man.

"I am Jade, the keeper of the present," he spoke, looking intently at me.

"I know that, but who are YOU? I mean, what's with the changing forms? Who are you? The real you?" I could feel two dozen eyes glued in my direction. I knew, that they knew already, that very soon I would be joining them in the time trap.

"I am the present, so I can be anything I choose." He shrugged and looked at me with a wisdom that could melt my soul.

"I can choose my reality today. You can't make choices about yesterday and you certainly can't choose for tomorrow but what you can choose is who you become today! And right now I choose to be a wise-old man, because that's what I need to be, to get to you," he smiled as he gently held my arm and urged me to walk with him towards the forest.

I heard a thump behind me. I knew it was the man with the bulging eyes. I knew the thump was a warning. I knew it meant: Don't go with Jade. I knew it meant: You will be trapped. I knew it meant: Run. And I walked on with Jade, the wise old man, who kept the present.

Warnings were useless now. I was already caught. I was already in Jade's custody. When he had the chance to tell me to run, the man with the bulging eyes was asking for help, and now when I did not have the chance, he was telling me to run. People are so confused. Timing is so important in life. The entire universe works on timing and keeps it, but we mortals take time for granted and mess things up for ourselves and for others.

Jade laughed, and his laughter stirred up a wind in the otherwise calm forest. "I can see that you met with Bomo, and what is amusing to me is that you survived Louihi. To survive Louihi is impressive, not many people make it from her." He looked in my direction, slightly impressed I thought, and added gleefully, "and as you can see, no one has made it back home from me."

Jade actually spoke with pride that he was more powerful than Bomo and Louihi. The keeper of the present implied with arrogance that he was more powerful than both the future and the past.

Jade took me towards where the trees began and directed my attention to a small pond-like area. "That's where we can sit and talk," he said, "knowing you, you have a lot to say," he said almost mockingly.

Yes, I had a lot to say. I did that for a living after all. And I suspected that sometimes in my whole need to talk, I missed out on what other people had to say. And because I didn't hear them, I lived by my assumption of what they thought, how they felt and what they wanted. This had probably been the start of my lonely life: I had so much to say that I forgot to listen.

Jade had not let go of my arm the whole time we walked towards the pond. I didn't know if he was being courteous or making sure I would not run away. "Sit here," he said, pointing towards a metal stump.

I heard faint thumps in the background and I knew that I was being led into the trap too. I had a good mind to walk over to the man with the bulging eyes and tell him to stop thumping. I wanted to tell him to use his energy to plan his own escape rather than disturb my peace. Not that I had any peace anyway, but he was disturbing me.

"I am the keeper of the present," Jade spoke with pride. "To leave from here, you have to be in one time, the present. There exists no other time in the universe except now. The past, like the future, does not exist. There is only one reality, the present. If you are not in the present, then you..." he said pointing towards me... "don't exist." Now his form changed into that of a butcher. "And if you don't exist, then how can you go back?" Jade, the wise old Jade, was gone. This butcher-like man stood in front of me in absolute mock and laughed till the wind grew stronger.

My heart was beating furiously. The thumping again started from all directions and I wanted to run. I wanted to run back.

The butcher now changed into a beautiful, gorgeous man, like a Greek God. This incredible-looking man bent over the pond and dipped his hands in it, teasing me to bathe with him. Under normal circumstances I would have been glad to comply but the sinister essence of Jade was very evident even behind the guise of this sensual man.

"If I must trap you, I must do it with the love you deserve," he spoke so eloquently, with so much sensual energy that I could not resist. He could have held out a cup of poison and I would have drunk it with a toast. The man obviously had me under his spell.

I heard a violent thumping in the background. As the Greek God withdrew his hand from the pond, a trail of sticky translucent liquid dripped from it. He touched the liquid to my head and in an instant a box of translucent solid formed around me. It was the exact same box of glass that had all the other men trapped. Jade had trapped me in time.

As I placed my hands on the transparent walls of my cell, Jade changed back to the wise old man. "This is a time trap," he said, proud of his creation. "You can see your thoughts reflect back to you on the walls from the inside."

As Jade spoke I could instantly see a film inside the cell. The walls had come alive with my thoughts. It was like watching a film in fast forward mode. I could see images whizzing past. The forest, Vicky, the blinking lights, my dogs, Bomo, Kurt, a dead body, my dead body, my skeletal form stuck in this cell. I could see an insane array of images, a combination of my past and my future.

"You are where your mind is," Jade spoke. "If you are not in the present, then you have no business being out in the world and pulling everyone into your world of non-existence. If you are not in the present, you have no business pulling others into your past. And if you are not in the present you will not only destroy your chances of the future but you will also destroy other people's present," Jade spoke with a hint of rage as I became dizzy with the thoughts and images racing inside the glass cell.

"The only way out is for you to be here, now, in present time. And with the looks of it," he laughed pointing at the others in their own traps, "you have eternity to get there."

And Jade abruptly disappeared.

I stood in my glass cell. I was all alone physically, but not mentally; I had the whole world inside the cell with me. A confused world. A world of a terror-stricken past and fear-stricken future. I was trapped. I was trapped in a place of non-existence. I was trapped in my past and my future and the only way out was to find my way into the present.

Jade had left; I wanted him to come back. I wanted to talk to him. I had not signed up for this. He had made a mistake. I was sent by

Kurt, I was just a stupid kid on the block. I wanted to go home. I had made a mistake. Kurt had made a mistake. Someone had made a terrible mistake here. I wanted to get out.

I did the last thing that would possibly help me. I began to cry. Crying only made my helplessness real. Crying was a public declaration of my helplessness and every tear I shed only made me weaker. "Stop it!" I shouted at myself. This was no time to be helpless; I had Vicky waiting at the edge of the forest. I had tied him up in time too. I had to pull my act together and get out of here. I guess sometimes we just can't see how many people are in waiting, how many people have put their lives on hold because of us. This was not the time to cry, this was the time to take control.

As I angrily wiped my tears, I caught a glimpse of Bomo. Jade, in the form of Bomo, was standing outside my cell. Bomo kept the future. He peered closer. "I cannot help you. You can see the future; you can keep your vision of the future, but you can't live in it. A future that is built on fear will destroy you in the future, as it will destroy you in the present."

"Bomo !" I yelped. Bomo could help me. But Bomo changed into Louihi. "You will amount to nothing. Your past will always be your reality. Your past will never leave you; it gives you company today and will give you company in the future," she mocked.

I was trapped. Jade was playing I-can-be-anyone-I-choose-to-be with his changing forms and that was only adding to my helplessness.

The images on the wall became clear. My face stung as I felt an angry slap from my father for a stupid, mindless mistake. I felt myself flung to the far wall of the cell as if it was really happening. Even though the slap was an image on the wall, I felt its sting on my face for real.

Even though my father had slapped me decades ago, I felt the pain right now in the present.

"You are where your mind is," Loha laughed with her teeth clanging. Jade was on a roll as my misery became his business.

As the sting on my face reduced, I saw my car racing at top speed and falling over the cliff. I fell and banged on the sides of the cell as my head smashed and the blood began to pour out of the side of my head. I began to cry out in pain. Every time I got on the highway, I had this image of my car going off the cliff in my head. Right now that image was literally killing me. My fear of the future was manifesting in my present. The accident was not only playing on the wall, it was killing me for real in the present.

"Even though the accident is just a fragment of your imagination, it is evidence of your fear. If you think of it today, it is your present," Bomo spoke again. Jade was using Bomo and Louihi's forms to mock me, to make a point that the past and the future mean nothing if I cannot be in the present.

As my head cleared up and the blood on the walls vanished, I staggered to stand up. One by one, as images of my past and my future visited my thoughts and played on the wall, I lived their impact in the present. My past repeated itself and I experienced a painful future even though it had never happened. I experienced the pain of my fears and I experienced the trauma of my negative thoughts.

With so much beating and battering, I sat in the cell, numb with the trauma, my head in my hands. This had to stop. I would die soon if this continued. Every single thought I had, whether it was about the past or the future, was coming alive in my present.

I realized that I did not actually have to be in a time trap to be at the mercy of my past or future. Every time I focused on the misfortunes of the past, I felt unfortunate in my present. And every time I had fears about my future, I ruined my present chance to make a difference. I had lived like this all my life without even knowing it.

A tap on the glass cell from the outside got my attention. I lifted my numb head and looked up, still lying down on the floor. I saw a man dressed in a business suit. His demeanor was sharp, his hair was pulled back, he wore glasses and looked like he meant business. It was Jade again, playing his I-am-the-keeper-of-the-present trick.

"Being in the present does not mean being oblivious to your future or not having a vision. What you see here is a future you have painted with your fears. It's not enough to just have a dream or a vision of a beautiful future, what is important is that you let go of the fear and doubt that you can create it. You never had the car accident that you played in your head but you became a potential liability for yourself and others on the road each time you took the wheel because you fed your vision with your fear. Your aspirations for the future are woven by threads of fear. No matter how much you dream or how much you dare, your fears about the past and future will come true for you today." He spoke like a corporate guru.

"You have to let go of the strings of the past that you so tightly hold to your heart. With Louihi you left the terrible past that you had created. To be in the present you also have to let go of the terrible past others created for you. You not only have to let go of the wrong you did to others, you also have to let go of the wrong others did to you. Your father hit you once and you have beaten yourself every single day of your present because you could not let go of the hurt he caused you in the past. You have to find a foothold in the present, where you can choose to be anything you want to be. The present is the only place for creation. Create or be destroyed." He spoke and disappeared before I could reach out and ask him to show me a way out.

I was stuck in time like everyone else and I did not know the way out. If I did not get out tonight, I knew I never would. Vicky would go back and my only hope of getting back would be gone. How was I going to get out of this trap?

Before I could complete my thought another image began playing on the wall. It was my grandfather's funeral. When he had died he had taken away my reason to live. The same agony and fear consumed me now. As I saw his body engulfed in the flames at the crematorium I said aloud, "Wait a minute!" and as if by magic, the image paused. It was strange that when I paused to look at the past, it paused on the wall too.

"Wait a minute," I frowned and got up. The image of my grandfather's cremation was stuck on the wall. In all my dramatization of loss and sadness I forgot to bid goodbye and bless the holy man's soul. In my feeling of loss I had forgotten to see the goodness and courage he had left behind with me as a virtue of his existence. My grandfather was gone in body but I had felt his essence all my life. I had mourned the loss of his body and I had forgotten to rejoice the life he had taught me to live. As the thought cleared in my head, the image on the wall disappeared. I felt a little more powerful than a few minutes ago.

I looked around; nobody was there. Suddenly another image was on the wall. I had always wanted to be super rich, a billionaire, but there was always an uncertainty about my own ability. There was a desire for abundance and yet there was no faith in my own power or the ability to create it. So in my present, I was neither rich nor able.

All desires remained desires. They created even more frustration and unhappiness in my present, because I had seen them and aspired for them but not acquired them. When I saw the frustrated, purposeless and unhappy presence that was me, I said, "Hey, wait a minute," holding the image still on the wall. The image froze on the wall.

I looked at my miserable self in that image and I protested, "I AM able. I am more able than I give myself credit for. But somehow in my whole charade of becoming a billionaire, I am not doing the things that will make me a billionaire. I desire to be a billionaire and yet I continue to live by my ordinary and daily ways. If I need a bigger future, then I need to do bigger things today. It's not true that I am not worthy of being a billionaire, I just have to do things that would make me worthy enough."

The image had started out making me feel small and unworthy. However, as my perspective changed, as my sense of control and power grew, the image faded away. It just faded away as though I had interrupted its course.

Before I could react or gather my thoughts, another painful image popped up. My ex-fiancé had left me for another woman. Before the image could go any further and drown me in a pool of depression again, I shouted, "Stop! I chose the wrong man for the wrong reasons. I chose him not because I loved him but because he satisfied a need that I myself could not fill. I needed someone to remind me that I was beautiful and that I was loved because I never found the beauty or love in me. Heck, I never loved myself. I loved the man because he loved me. The relationship was headed for disaster from day one." What surprised me was that the image did not move any further and disappeared without playing out further.

More images popped up, this time at longer intervals than before. And each time an image popped up, I was alert, armed with responsibility. No matter what thought was reflected upon the wall, I took immediate responsibility for all the contents in the thought. No blame, no criticism, no feeling like a victim, no drama, just plain responsibility for all that had happened! And the minute I took responsibility the effect of the thought disappeared.

I spent hours, though it seemed like years. The images came and the images went. I kept standing up, owning up, growing bigger, and growing powerful with every thought that popped its head onto the walls. And soon I was standing tall in front of the wall like a winning warrior. "Bring it on! Bring down the past and pour down the future, because I know that there is only one point of creation of any reality: RESPONSIBILITY. And when I am armed with responsibility there is nothing that can shake my ground today. Even if I goofed up in the past, as long as I take responsibility, I can do something about it TODAY that will make me bigger. Even if I have fears about the future, as long as I take responsibility, I can do something about it TODAY that will make me bigger. Because creation is a 'present time phenomena'. I own the present and as long as I am here, I can change the past and create a future," I assured myself.

I stood inside the cell with more power than I had ever felt in my whole life. I felt the power flowing through my veins. The images suddenly stopped. There was nothing. There was nothing whatsoever on the walls. Not one speck of an image. A cold breeze blew and I shivered. Where did the cold breeze come from? I stretched out my hand and it went right through the wall. Wait a minute, there was no wall. I was FREE! I was FREE!!! I danced. I was free. I ran around from where I stood. I was FREE!!! I had broken the time trap. I was in the present.

Where was Jade? "Jade!" I shouted out to him. Did he see that? Could he see how powerful I had become? "Jade!" I shouted. "I am free Jade," I danced.

"I can see that," a little boy giggled behind me.

"Jade, be the old man! I want to talk to the old wise man!" I laughed.

"I can only talk to you at your present level" the boy grinned and danced. "And when you are in the present, you are not old and withering; you are child like, young, free and new!" He clapped his hands in acknowledgement of my freedom.

"I am going home. I am going to live to tell." I almost picked Jade up in my arms and swung him around in delight. Jade only giggled and laughed like a child, reflecting my own state as he did.

"The answer was so easy, Jade," I stopped and held his hand. Jade changed to the wise old man I wanted to talk to. "When I take responsibility over the past and the future, I find myself in the present," I smiled with tears of joy.

"The answer is one that evades generations for lifetimes. Taking responsibility is by far one of the most difficult things to do. So difficult that people would rather die in a time trap blaming others than own up for their own lot in life," he said pointing to a billion people outside of the forest.

"Life can only be lived in the present. And it's a beautiful life if you care to create it. But when the past and the future take our attention from the present, we lead the whole planet towards disaster," Jade was now walking with me towards the lake.

"You have broken the time trap. And when you break the time trap, you become invincible. You can choose and be anyone you want to, you can have anything you want. It's in the present that you are truly free; a free person, a free spirit, a free essence reflecting the might of the universe. Now run along, and live," Jade smiled excitedly, changing back to the innocent boy.

I began to run towards the lake. I had to catch the boat and go back home. Before I could run away, I heard a thump. I turned around and saw the dozen old men stuck in time. I ran up to the man with the bulging eyes, his eyes popping with disbelief that I was free.

"You can break the trap. You can be in the present. Just take responsibility over all that has happened and all that ever will be!" I spoke to him frantically.

He looked at me blankly and then in one instant I saw his eye spark and he grinned a grin that only a man who had seen the light could.

"I can take responsibility!" he said slowly as tears built up in his big sunken eyes. "I can take responsibility," he whispered as he choked.

I looked at all the men in all the traps. "TAKE RESPONSIBILITY," I shouted as I cupped my hands and the words echoed joyfully in the whole forest. I knew they would be free for I knew that owning up and taking responsibility is real freedom.

I ran towards the lake where the boat was waiting for me. Jade, the little boy, was holding it for me.

"The boat will lead you to your way out of the forest," Jade said playfully. He pushed it and waved me goodbye as his eyes danced with joy.

I ran back to the forest and found the exact spot where I had left my coat and thermals. I picked them up and plunged myself into the darkness. Suddenly it was not important whether Vicky was on the other side. It was not important whether I could see the light or not. What was important was that I stood confidently in present time willing to create, handle, and own any circumstance that came my way.

The journey back to the last wall of trees was magical. When I was immersed in my power, the forest bowed. I stepped out of the last embrace of the trees and in the distance I saw the dimming blinkers of the car. There were three cars there, not just one. I shouted out "Vicky" and half a dozen flashlights shone my way. I covered my eyes and there was darkness again. I saw a gigantic figure running my way followed by a few others.

It was Vicky. He was running and he embraced me in disbelief, almost setting my hair on fire with the cigarette in his hand.

"You made it," he whispered and laughed.

When you make it back, it makes other people's wait worthwhile. What we do not realize is that when we get stuck in time, we trap many others in time too.

"I knew it. I knew it all along," Vicky said, as he nodded to the other four men who had come there to support him in his crazy mission to support me.

CHAPTER 11 /

Back Home

Vicky would just not let me loose from his embrace. The other men also came towards us, cheering. Before I could announce that I had met Jade, one man thrust a photograph in my hand. "Did you see him?" he asked with hope in his eyes. He looked at me eagerly as though asking for a missing family member.

I took the picture from the man's hand and my face lit up when I saw it. It was the same man with the bulging eyes. He looked so different in the picture, almost handsome. And yet the man I saw in the forest was a man beaten in time.

The other men also had come with pictures and though I did not get a good look at the other guys in the time trap, I assured them that they were possibly alive, just trapped.

It was uncanny that in a foreign land, by virtue of my purpose, I had built such a strong bond with total strangers. Sometimes purpose creates an intimacy that brings people together in a way that casual or even professional encounters can never do. Nobody had any selfish agenda or money to make; we were connected by our innate courage, love, and unity. Vicky had helped me out of sheer humanity. Smith had not even charged me money for the taxi drop. Vicky was out burning his fuel and wasting his night in support of a total stranger with a crazy mission.

I spent the entire ride back to the Hotel Continental explaining how I made it into the Deborence forest and my encounter with Jade and the others caught in the time trap. When I narrated how I had gotten out of the time trap it brought tears to Vicky's eyes. He quickly crossed his heart. "I am glad that you are back," he said, touching my hand from across the seat.

The pretty receptionist at the Continental was happy to see me when I went to collect my bags. She did not ask me if I had found my way into the Deborence forest. Since she had already said that no one ever came back, she must have drawn her own conclusions. But Vicky was eagerly speaking with her in French and with the look that I saw on her face, I knew that Vicky had told her. I did not have the €10 to pay for my bags and the receptionist just waved to me in a manner which said, "Don't bother about the money; I am happy you are alive." She picked up the phone and began to talk excitedly to someone at the other end.

"Let's get you out of here before the paparazzi gets you," Vicky winked.

It was nice of Vicky to drop me to the airport without charging me any money whatsoever. "That is the least I can do for you, to show respect for your courage," he said as we said our goodbyes at the airport.

Before I turned my back on Zurich, I secretly wished that the others caught in the time trap would find their way back to the present too.

It would certainly take a very determined seeker to go into the forest of no return looking for answers. I believed that all the men who went into Deborence did so on a personal mission, a personal quest. One does not stumble into the time trap by accident. I just hoped that whatever courage and seeking had led them there would help them take responsibility for their past and future, and that they would be able to find their way back into the present. And knowing Jade and his ways, I knew that even though they were trapped in time, they were in good company.

Veni met me at the entrance and she was absolutely delighted to see me. She embraced me and I could see genuine joy in her eyes. It seemed as though she was partaking of my victory. Veni would fly back home with me. Kurt had booked me in business class. "You have moved from a Jet plane to Malaysia, to economy to Zurich and now to business class back home. There has to be variety, right?" Veni chuckled as we checked in. "By the way," she added with a grin, "a private Jet from Zurich to India would cost $25,000."

We chatted a long time until Veni fell fast asleep. Something told me that this had been as much an adventure for Veni as it had been for me.

I could not believe that soon I would return to my familiar world. I would return with a brand new me, with a changed perspective about who I was and how I viewed my life. And somewhere deep down inside I hoped for another adventure. I would not mind being thrown off the aircraft or even for that matter into the deep sea. I realized that I had absolutely loved every moment of the last seven days that I had spent on a mission called 'me'.

I just could not wait to meet Kurt. I could not wait to tell him all my stories. Maybe he already knew them, but what the heck, I would love to tell him anyways. And . . . I had a lot of questions to ask. Since the 'seminar' would technically end tomorrow, I would demand some answers. And no matter what he said, I would not take no for an answer.

Just as I was about to close my eyes, breathe a sigh of relief, and go off to sleep, the airhostess tapped my shoulder gently and said, "I have a message for you, Miss Kumar." I almost jumped out of my skin. I thought I was done with all the messages, I thought I was done with all the assignments. I sat up straight and rubbed my eyes, "What is it?" I asked her curiously. The airhostess was holding a brown envelope in her hand. I took it from her and tore it open as she walked away.

It was a letter from Kurt:

Priya,

This flight is your flight to freedom. Where you go from here is your journey to decide. You are hours away from earning your license to live and the world awaits your ride.

I will see you tomorrow at 4.32 a.m. to complete the circle. If you are on time, consider yourself late.

Love and Prayers,

~ Kurt Rinck

P.S. Please turn in your "My License to Live" Journal at Check In at the Taj Villas.

I smiled while reading the letter and glanced over at Veni. She was fast asleep. I put away the letter and was about to go back to sleep when I sat up with a jolt. I had not filled my journal. I needed to spend time writing, reflecting. It seemed to me that from now on I would always continue to write and I would always continue to grow. Our actions don't make us divine, the intention and purpose of our actions do. So many of us work without paying attention to the intention and purpose. I was going to be different.

I sat up straight and headed for the overhead compartment. I picked out the journal from my bag and much to my neighbor's annoyance I switched on the reading light to jot down my thoughts. I took the pen and bit the tip for many a minute reminiscing about the entire day before I started to write.

> *I feel very powerful. I know that I have completed Kurt's assignment and whether he says it or not, I know I have earned my License to Live, by my own standards. I can now see what Kurt saw when I first met him. I would never have admitted that I was living my life recklessly. I was beginning to live and believe in my lie that I was in control. I was far from that. But today I have found myself. I have found my truth and I know it is for real.*

> *My life seven days ago seems like a distant past. It seems so distant that I am having second thoughts about whether it was really me who was living it. I started out with fear, doubt and cynicism and I have ended my journey with courage, certainty and gratitude.*

> *I am grateful to all the people who supported me in my journey to finding Jade. I would not have made it without them. I have realized that in life there is a BIG purpose and then there are daily smaller purposes that may seem*

disconnected from our bigger purpose, but if we expand our vision to embrace the world, then we can see how every event and every person is connected to bring us closer to our purpose and our destiny.

Even though Uma and Karlos were not here I learnt that I could handle people and take responsibility without deviating from my own purpose and values.

I was afraid of going into the Deborence forest. Not only was finding Jade a difficult task, but getting to Jade was even more dangerous. It was more dangerous than jumping off an aircraft. Death is better than being trapped in time forever. Somehow I learnt that only a seeker would venture into places where others fear to tread. I learnt that just by being determined to move on and not look back, half the battle of fear and doubt is won. I learnt that when people live in fear they spread it. I learnt that it takes one person with courage to liberate others of their imaginary demons.

I learnt that there is always a way out. You come out of the trap of the past when you take responsibility for all your actions and intentions. When you take responsibility for every moment of your life, then you are free from your past. I learnt that you could also break the trap of the fearful future by taking responsibility to act today in accordance with what you really want. To desire a different future and to act out of your past fears will not only mess up the present but also keep you trapped in time.

My greatest joy in meeting Jade has been that I can create any possibility I want. I can choose to be anyone that I desire in the present moment. I can chose to be a billionaire if I want to. If I behave like one, think like one and do like one, I will then soon become one for real. And a billionaire will become a pauper the day he stops behaving like one, thinking like one and doing like one. It's not a lesson that I have merely learnt; it's a lesson that I have become.

I am happy that I am going home and I know that I will always find a way to be continually seeking and continually challenging myself.

I think my greatest victory has been the realization that all that I am writing I have always known all along. I had just stopped looking. I know I will continue writing everyday and that everyday will be a spiritually enlightening day. Instead of reading other people's story, if I just write mine at the end of every day, I will create a better life for myself."

CHAPTER 12 /

Completing the Circle

Arriving at the Taj Villas, I felt as though I was returning home after years of separation. The drive from the airport to the hotel seemed the longest journey in the entire seven days. For me, time always seems to have slowed in its tracks when I am anticipating something. Veni was sleepy during the entire drive and even though her eyes were open; her whole being was fast asleep. I could almost see a 'do not disturb' sign on her face. I had so much to tell her but Veni was apparently asleep. There was a volcano of stories ready to explode in me. I wanted to run and tell the whole world about my adventures, about Kurt's 'seminar' and my meeting with strange wise people. Right now the taxi driver was letting out a lazy yawn, quite happy to give us a ride and make money in the wee hours of the day.

By nature I'm a 'teller'. I have to tell everything to everyone. Sometimes my mother wonders if I can ever keep a secret. At this moment, I wanted to catch the first person I could and tell him everything about Bomo, Louihi and Jade. I wanted to shake up everyone from their slumber and shout in their ears, "You can be free." I had so much excitement flowing through my veins that I could have exploded out of my own energy.

It was only 3 a.m. when we arrived at the hotel. Veni had a trail of saliva flowing down her chin. The woman was really tired, I thought. As I went up to the reception, I was startled to see Karlos and Uma there. They were waiting for me. Uma ran up to me just like Betty and Coco, and gave me a hug.

"I have been waiting for you all night," she said, smiling, still holding on to me. "I'm so happy you made it."

"What are you guys doing here?" I looked at Karlos who had a very distinct black eye. "For the same reason you are here," Karlos said, "To meet Kurt!"

"Oh," I was a little surprised. "I thought you guys had left."

"We thought we were out too," Uma said. "But Kurt's seminar is like the mafia, you can change course but you cannot quit."

"I don't understand," I said, puzzled. What did she mean? Where were they all this time?

"Come," Uma said, taking my bag from my hand. "We arrived a couple of hours ago. Why don't you turn your journal in and we can go and chat over a cup of tea."

I handed my journal to Veni. "I'm going to bed. I'm not needed until morning. You can collect your belongings from me after you meet with Kurt," Veni spoke sleepily.

Karlos, Uma and I went up to the beach, to where the seminar area had been seven days ago. We sat on the sand, watching the waves crash in the distance.

"So did you meet Jade?" Uma asked excitedly. "It's unfortunate that I did not meet Bomo or Jade!"

"Why did you lie, Uma?" I confronted her, totally ignoring her excitement and interest in my victory, since I thought that an explanation was long overdue. I was probably more impatient to hear her part of the story than to tell her mine.

"I'm sorry," Uma said, and by the tone of her voice I knew that she meant it. "I'm sorry I ran away. I was so obsessed with completing the assignment and finding Bomo that I abandoned you and Karlos." Karlos gave her a look that spelt traitor and they both smiled and giggled. "But you were dead Karlos, and life had to move on!" Uma giggled. Karlos threatened to jump on her and we all laughed. I guess Uma and Karlos had had the time to clear their misunderstandings.

"I got caught by the cops when I ran away and Veni had to come and bail me out," Uma confessed.

"Oh, but you came to us with the cops . . ." I was confused.

"Yes, I had failed the assignment and broken the rules. I was pulled out of the assignment. And because I was out, I was given a new assignment; to continue on a new track. And my new assignment was to be a thorn in your flesh!" Uma spoke to me apologetically.

I got it. I so got it. Kurt did not believe in throwing people out when they failed an assignment. He merely plucked them out of the assignment they failed at and plugged them into another. So either way, they continued the journey, learning different lessons, lessons they were ready to accept and learn.

"My assignment was to challenge you, to give you a hard time, to mislead you, to irritate you, basically to make life difficult for you. It was the hardest thing I have ever done in my whole life because you are such a nice person. I adore you, even though you may not believe it. To be tough on you was my greatest learning—that sometimes for someone else to learn, you have to be tough on him or her. I hated being nasty to you but I knew that my actions were directed towards your evolution as a better person." Uma spoke with compassion rare in a girl her age.

"I learnt from Louihi through you. Your victory was my lesson. I could learn it because I did not allow my personal emotions of being a bitch towards you, interfere with my role in the assignment. From there I was assigned to Karlos." Uma now giggled and looked at Karlos.

"And you, Karlos, what have you been up to? You and Uma were on the assignment together?" I was curious now. I had obviously missed something. Or rather, we all were at the exact place we were meant to be.

"Oh, Kurt gave me a tougher time than I thought I deserved. At one point I felt that maybe being on the original assignment would have been much easier," Karlos spoke vehemently. I understood his emotion. I felt the same way actually. I didn't know what Karlos had been through, but for me, my assignment was the greatest and most difficult one. Opinion and perception is a very personal thing, and so is life and success.

"I had to go and meet my ex-wife in Hong Kong and confess all my wrong doing to her," Karlos smiled. Uma pointed to his black eye and they both laughed.

"And boy," Uma said, "how she beat him up. We had to call the cops because the woman would have killed him!" Uma spoke with alarm.

"I guess I had caved myself under the guilt of cheating on my wife and being the worst husband anyone could ever deserve. Even after years of separation, I was never able to look at myself as worthy of any woman's love. I buried myself in work and built a multinational corporation, but the riches that came my way could not fill up the loneliness or shame that I felt inside," Karlos spoke calmly.

Karlos had changed. This was not the same man I had met when I left from Genting. Karlos had certainly changed. He had a different energy and vibe about him. He seemed a man who had taken charge of his life and had found the ability to confront himself.

"And even though she beat me, I felt that I deserved it!" Karlos continued. "That outburst was long overdue. I feel happy that I have paid my dues and now I can move on! I feel new already!" He beamed.

"If it were not for Uma," he pointed to Uma, as she smiled in acknowledgement, "I would have been dead!"

"His ex-wife had pulled out a pistol when Karlos told her about the 'other women' in his life. She almost pulled the trigger and I had to jump in and control her. Karlos just stood there!" She waved her arms up in the air in frustration. "He did not fight or try to stop her!" she spoke animatedly.

Karlos just smiled. "That confrontation was long pending. I knew that she would react this way and that is why I never told her all these years. I was afraid she would kill me when she heard the truth. I died every day in guilt, hiding the lie."

"It's over now!" Karlos finally announced. "I'm a free man!" He got up and stretched out his arms to the world.

"How was your meeting with Jade?" Uma tugged at my arm. "And what about Bomo?" She was eager to know but I found myself at a loss for words. As much as I wanted to tell, I did not know where to start and what to say.

We sat for about an hour, chatting, watching the waves, laughing, crying, hugging and drinking tea. The fatigue was gone; the wisdom of the past seven days had sunk in.

Veni appeared with more tea. She looked fresher. I knew that make up always helps but Veni did not wear any. "Does Kurt need to be woken up?" I winked at her.

"Ah," she said looking at her watch, it was 4.15 a.m. "Mr. Rinck is already waiting for you!"

"Waiting for me? Where?" I looked around. There was no fat man in sight. Kurt was too large to miss, and we had been here for over an hour, at the seminar area.

"Where is Kurt?" I asked Veni again with a little concern in my voice. I was preparing to run in any direction that she would point in.

"Oh!" Veni looked surprised. "Mr. Rinck said you would know where to find him!"

"How would I know where to find him?" I looked at Uma and Karlos if they knew something.

"I don't know," Karlos shrugged. "We are meeting him at 6 a.m."

"What?" I was confused. Kurt wanted to meet me alone, obviously it made sense. I was on the assignment alone. But where?

Suddenly, I knew. Without a word I broke into a run. My car was in the parking lot. I barked at the valet to bring it in a hurry. I sat in my car and pumped the accelerator, and with the tires screeching I shot out of the hotel. It was 4.18 a.m. and I had twelve minutes to make it to the seaway.

CHAPTER 13 /

Connecting the Dots

As I raced towards the seaway and approached the bridge, I saw the silver Jaguar parked right behind the 'Under Construction' sign. I brought my car to a screeching halt behind it. My eyes searched in the dark and I found him, exactly where I had stood seven days ago. Kurt Rinck was standing at the edge of the pavement facing the sea, his back turned towards me. He was wearing the same black t-shirt and his name KURT sparkled in silver on the back. The stars shone on him as he stood still in time.

I stepped up on the ledge and Kurt spun around with a smile. He raised his eyebrows as he pointed to the dial of his diamond-studded Rolex, "You are late!"

Well, I was in time but according to Kurt I was late. I knew the rule and did not want to argue with him. "I am sorry, Kurt," I said, hardly meaning it. I was just way too delighted to be there and to have completed my assignment.

Kurt opened his arms and invited me into an embrace. I was lost in his large form. Embracing Kurt was like being consumed by the whole universe. It was like feeling complete. I guess being here with Kurt was my greatest reward; to earn a place in his heart.

"Being early," Kurt spoke as he held me by the shoulder and looked towards the horizon, "is the mark of a creator. The only entity that came before creation was the creator himself. When you show up earlier than the expected time of arrival, you have more opportunities than you will ever know. As the norm would have it, the master is supposed to show up after the student has arrived. But a master is a master because he arrives before the student shows up. The student remains a student because the master has already shown up. You become the master when you show up earlier than expected, faster than expected, and stick around longer after the others have gone."

I stared at Kurt and I could see the wisdom in his words.

"You did it!" he said, looking straight into my eyes. There they were! The kindest blue eyes in the whole world. "You did it!" he said, laughing out to the sky. "Boy, you have some grit!" He shook his head.

I smiled sheepishly, now blushing at my own achievement. Kurt sat down on the ledge and the waves came and kissed the tips of his dangling feet as they rose and then fell back again into the dark sea.

"A lot of people feel that my methods of coaching are severe," Kurt spoke with a softness that belied any such criticism. "But you see, when someone pays me $25,000 to change their life, it does call for some severe responsibility on my part to do it. The greater the responsibility, the greater is the intensity in executing it. And often my intensity is interpreted as severe. I am not here to please anyone. And I can't push you to introspect and change by singing songs with you and chanting mantras in your ears. I do it by pushing you in places you have stopped looking, because they held those parts of your life you did not want to see! And sometimes to get you to confront that which you have been avoiding takes some severe persuasion." Kurt tapped his heart and winked.

"I can see it, Kurt. I can see that I have grown in every sense that counts in the past week. You will not believe it but the past seven days have made me spiritually, emotionally, and mentally more stable and alert. I am bigger and taller than when I started out. I had started out as a skeptic. A skeptic of my own greatness. And I have ended a believer. A believer of my own divinity. I will never be able to thank you enough, Kurt." I had so much to say, so much to tell him but right now all that was welling out of my mouth was gratitude.

Kurt looked at me and acknowledged my gratitude with a smile. That's it; just a smile. I looked on towards the horizon. The moon was nowhere in sight but the stars shone on gleefully in a pale sky. Soon the earth would spin and embrace the sun.

"You know the funny part about the past seven days?" Kurt spoke softly as though letting me into a very well-guarded secret. "Well, you all were assigned tasks. You all started on the same page, with the same instructions, but somewhere along the course you all parted in the direction of your greatest lessons. Karlos had different lessons to learn. He had a different part of the jigsaw missing in his life. Uma had a different calling and a different learning. She instinctively drifted in that direction. You, on the other hand, were determined on your journey. You were led where your lesson awaited you. So even though the three of you were on different tracks during the course of the seminar, all three of you emerged bigger. And even if the three of you were at the same place and the same time, the three of you would have grown in different ways. I allowed you to be led to your calling, and doing that sometimes is really expensive and that's why the $25,000," Kurt explained as though sharing his heart, and I could feel it. I could feel his heart in every word he said. Only a true master would allow his students to learn what they needed most and not what the master needed to teach most. Whoever called Kurt a 'fine coach' was obviously selling him short. Kurt was the greatest master I had ever met.

Karlos and Uma had not failed because they did not meet Bomo. Karlos and Uma had merely changed tracks towards their healing. Just because people were not on my track, just because they were not in my company or could not understand what I was envisioning, did not mean that they had failed or that they were small or that they should be out of my zone of compassion. When people choose to divert from our thinking, our way of working, our pace and style, it just means that they are on different tracks to being good people. I have lost out on so many friends just because they could not keep pace with me or understand me. I felt foolish now because I could see that I was the foolish one to expect them to follow my way. Karlos found his liberation in Hong Kong just as I had found mine with Jade. Uma had found her peace in serving Karlos just as I had found mine with Bomo. So who was bigger and who was smaller? All of us emerged bigger.

"Your true self emerges when you put your fake identities and distractions aside. You can never discover your greatness behind an identity card and you can never truly communicate with another if you have not had a serious conversation with yourself. And by the way," Kurt said abruptly, "Veni watched your back with legalities in every country you went to," Kurt spoke with deep respect for Veni. Veni had looked haggard and tired and I was beginning to understand why.

"But it was important to get you to think about who you really are and what you actually need to get along in life. You are enough all by yourself. There is only one person that can make you or break you and that is you. To trust and to believe in yourself, you have to know that you have the ability to pull yourself out of any situation. A person who can count on himself has become a creator, a true master, a true friend."

Letting go of my identity was the most difficult part for me. My position had defined me for so long that taking away my status and designation and identity actually shook my foundation and confidence. People who rose to greatness did not do so based on their titles; they did so based on their creation. Somewhere along the line I had begun to equate title and identity with greatness. I nodded to no one in particular as the lesson made its mark in my heart.

"Bomo, Louihi and Jade exist, but no one expects you to find them. Only a seeker, a true seeker will allow himself or herself to be led. And seeking is your hearts calling, not my assignment for you to follow. It was impossible for you to find the keepers of time if you were merely on my assignment. You started on my assignment but somewhere along the way you had embarked on your own journey," Kurt said. He was wise and I had deep admiration for him even though I did not openly want to admit it.

As I stared at the waves that danced towards my feet it made sense to me. Kurt's assignment had somewhere become MY mission. I was lost when I had started and I was so determined in my search for meaning that every task became my purpose. And I guess when we find our purpose in our daily tasks we come through the impossible and create the unbelievable.

"Kurt, you made us jump from an aircraft! I could have died!" I exclaimed, smiling, adding a little drama by waving my hands. Veni was watching our backs with legalities but what if I had died in the jump. I wanted to know what Kurt was thinking and just for fun I wanted to push Kurt off the ledge for him to get a feel of his own assignment.

"But you didn't!" Kurt pointed at me and brought my mental mischief to an abrupt halt. Damn, the man always got the better of me.

"Karlos almost died Kurt!" I blurted.

"Karlos had died a long time ago. Karlos had stopped living since many years. It would not take a very wise man to figure that he was just waiting to die. Karlos needed to learn to live again, and he does now!" I shuddered at Kurt's words.

"You have earned your License to Live," Kurt smiled. "I can say that even without reading your journal. Your journal is for you to keep, for you to maintain for the rest of your life. If you would just keep your own evaluation of a day well lived, you would be successful every day. And even if you achieved nothing and even if you lost everything you owned, as long as you fill a page in your journal in reflection and introspection, you are a winner. Success is not always about achievement; success is also in reflection and owning up responsibility." He winked.

I had heavily loaded the journal with a lot of lessons. Actually, writing the journal was a great idea after all. I realized that in writing I was learning twice, first in experience and then in reflection. I was quite happy to get it back because I really wanted to keep it. It kept my life's lessons, and I needed to revise some!

"Were they for real, Kurt? The keepers of time? Were Bomo, Louihi and Jade for real?" I asked. At this point, back in the spot where I had sat in a confused state seven days before, my experiences seemed almost magical, almost unreal.

"You met them, didn't you? You spoke to them, didn't you? They brought some clarity in your life. They transported you from being lost to finding yourself! What is real to you? Where is the real world? The world that tells you that you are smaller than you are? The world that teaches you to hide, the world that teaches you to pretend? The world that keeps you confined in arrogance and distractions? Is that real for you? You live amongst a population that is lost in time and their business is to keep you lost. Now that seems inexplicable to me, almost unreal! Which part of reality you chose to live in, is entirely in your hands. Whether you meet Bomo or not, your future still lies in front of you. Whether you live in fear of it or create your present out of it, is still in your hands. So is Bomo real? Whether you meet Louihi or not, your past still clutched you back and kept you away from the light. Whether you acknowledge Louihi or not, you never found yourself rejoicing in the good memories that Loha kept, you chained yourself with the wrath of Louihi. Is she real or not in your life? And whether you acknowledge it or not, you were trapped in time. The fact that you were lost and not happy with where you were, you were lost in time. Shrivelling away day by day, just like those people in the time trap. You would never know the power Jade held to be anyone you wished to be because you were never in present time. Was Jade or his absence from your life real for you? Which world have you been living in, young lady?" Kurt tapped my arm as he said that as though to make sure I was listening.

"There is a magical world of greatness and then there is a reality that keeps you chained in wretched existence. Which one will become real for you is the one you acknowledge!" Kurt coughed as he spoke. The man had more passion than I had ever seen in anyone. I could see how Kurt had allowed me my own learning without even being there, without even saying a single word.

"You earn your License to Live when you learn that there is only one keeper of time, and that is you! Bomo, Louihi, Jade are all within you. The one that you need to empower is Jade. The one that you need to keep a tab on is Bomo and the one that you need to cherish is Loha. Louihi is what you must let go of. When you become the keeper of your time, you become the keeper of your life!"

Kurt put one leg up on the ledge and drew a circle in the loose mud on it. "You are here in time," he said making a dot in the centre of the circle. And you are here only if you are in the present. If you are not in the present, you are not even in the game. You are somewhere else, sort of like lost in time. And when you are lost no one can tell where you are, not even you. So here you are," he said pointing to the dot. "And from here you have in front of you infinite possibilities," he said, drawing lines from the dot like you draw rays of sunshine emerging from the sun. "Anywhere you turn," he said, now placing the finger in the dot and turning it around, "anywhere you turn, anywhere you look, any direction you point to, you create possibilities. It is from this point in the present that you can do, be, and have anything that you desire." Kurt smiled, looking at me intently.

"Your License to Live is symbolic; it represents the power to create your realities. And the beauty about people living in present time is that they liberate others by their mere presence," Kurt said. I spotted a shooting star behind him and I gasped.

Kurt was silent for a while, allowing me to absorb what he had said. I did not feel lost anymore. I knew I was in control. The past no longer bothered me and I knew with absolute certainty that I could create any future I wanted. But I still had questions. I broke the silence finally.

"Have you met Jade, Kurt?" I was curious. "I loved Jade the most from all the Keeper's of Time. He was the toughest one to get past!"

"How does my meeting with Jade or not change what you learnt from him?" Kurt asked me a question back. "Why must my learning or lack of it complete yours? Is your meeting with Jade not enough for your learning? Why must you live in curiosity about others? What would it take for you to direct your curiosity inwards, towards your own greatness? A whole universe exists inside you. You don't have to go to the moon to understand the earth or the universe; you just have to look within! And yes, if you can't get past Jade, life goes past you. There is no life except in the present. Jade is my favorite keeper of time too." Kurt smiled, softening his voice and his tone.

Sometimes the answer Kurt gave was not the one I wanted to hear, but his answer certainly pointed me in the direction I needed to direct my attention to in order to get an answer for myself. Just conversing with Kurt was like enrolling for a spiritually loaded seminar.

"What if I had not got out of Deborence, Kurt? What if I had been trapped in time forever?" I wanted to know whether Kurt knew that I would make it back.

"What if . . . can go on forever! There is really no answer to what if! What if you had died in that car accident you had years ago? What if you had been married by now? What if you had never come for my seminar? And the 'what ifs' have no end! What if you had been stuck in time? Well, then you would have been stuck in time. You entered the forest of your own volition. You were determined to find out what I saw in you and you were determined to find you for yourself. You were determined to get out even before you got in, else you would never have had the courage to get into the Deborence forest. There is only one person who decides what happens to you and that is you. I can only give you instructions and you can choose to discard them as Uma and Karlos did. But you chose to follow. Was it my instructions you followed? Or was it your heart? I believe it was the latter. And when you follow your heart you can get out of anywhere, forget Deborence." Kurt spoke in one breath and I was amazed.

For the last seven days I had believed that I was following Kurt's instructions but what I was actually doing was following my heart. I had stopped doing that a long time ago. Since many years I was just following instructions, doing what I had to do, with no heart at all. Life had become mundane and life had become a rut. But I had found passion again. I had found life and adventure. I had led myself from being lost to being found and I had done it all by myself.

"And what about all the people trapped in time, Kurt? Was I the only one who ever got out? Won't those people ever get out?" I shuddered as I remembered the man with the bulging eyes, and the others, in the forest.

"Look around you and you will see a planet full of people trapped in time; banging walls and screaming and begging to be rescued. Look around and you will see that you really don't have to go to Deborence to meet them. If you can't be in the present, if you can't let go of the limiting and painful past, if you can't see a bright future, then you are trapped. Well, Deborence is a myth like success and life on earth. You break a myth by telling the truth and by living the truth. The truth is: nothing 'happens to us'; we 'make things happen'. When those people in Deborence see it, they will be liberated and when those people who surround you see it, they will be liberated too. When? When will they be free? When they choose to see the truth about their own power!" Kurt spoke, pausing to smile at me occasionally. His scanty hair was getting messed up in the early morning breeze and he looked sort of cute.

I wondered about Kurt. I wondered what made him do what he did. I don't think he realized it but his crazy ways had changed the way I looked at my life forever. Kurt caught my gaze and raised an eyebrow, sort of saying, "now what?"

"Kurt," I said and held his arm to get his attention. "What's your story Kurt? Who are you?" I wanted to know Kurt. I felt drawn to him, like a faithful disciple to his master.

"My story does not matter. You paid the $25,000 to write your story, the one you owe to yourself. I have been around and am getting around my own purpose. The real story is, will you get around yours? You can know me at your time; right now you are on my time. And in my turf, your story is my responsibility." Kurt grinned.

Damn it he always got away with answers. Maybe I could invite him for a coffee later in the day and get to know him better. I had so many questions in my head before I met Kurt and now they all seemed irrelevant. I guess I would let the answers unfold in time.

"So how does this end for you? What's your story from here?" Kurt asked me my question back while putting his arm around me. Just being in his embrace brought a feeling of wellness. I knew if I had even this man's shadow on my life, I would shine brighter than the brightest star.

"I was lost, Kurt. When I met you I was lost," I admitted though I knew that Kurt was aware of that from the first instance that he met me. "Even though I was successful above the surface, beneath I was hollow. But now . . . I know that with every step that I took forward, my past would trudge along with me. It tainted my future. It created doubt in my present. It stole my happiness. It brought guilt in my glory and it brought more misery in my success. I was never truly happy, Kurt. And I never understood why. How could I be happy when my past was ruling my future and unsettling my present? But now, I have seen it. I have seen the enemy within. I have left Louihi behind with all my troublesome past. Bomo cleared my doubts about my future and I saw that despite all my miserable doings I could still be worthy of a great future. And in finding Jade I found power in my present. I can never be beaten again, Kurt. There is no one and no circumstance that can ever pull me down. If I own up to every reality that I create, then if I don't like it, I can create another. I will never be a victim again. I will never be small again because I can create. A creator is never miserable. I now think and choose and decide out of a greater knowing than just being a slave to my past. I am bigger and I will only be bigger and greater with time." I stretched my arms out to show Kurt how big I would be and we both laughed.

"That's a beautiful ring," Kurt said catching the diamond shining on my finger. Ever since I had worn it, it sure had gotten a lot of attention.

"I got it from the future," I chuckled as I slipped it off my finger for Kurt to see. "Bomo got it for me as evidence of my future."

Kurt looked amused. "You must have made quite an impression on the old man for him to steal things from the future." He looked at me, cocking his head, "You have got some helluva man waiting for you in the future," he said, placing the ring on my palm and closing it with his other hand.

"It's time for me to go," he said, getting up. "The others are waiting for me." He put his hand in his pocket and held out a card. "It's your License to Live," he said as he handed me a shining gold card similar to my driving license, only this was real gold. I grabbed the card from Kurt's hand. It was lovely. It had the following embossed on it:

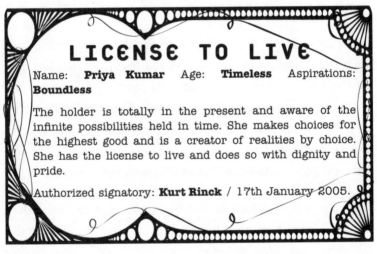

> # LICENSE TO LIVE
>
> Name: **Priya Kumar**   Age: **Timeless**   Aspirations: **Boundless**
>
> The holder is totally in the present and aware of the infinite possibilities held in time. She makes choices for the highest good and is a creator of realities by choice. She has the license to live and does so with dignity and pride.
>
> Authorized signatory: **Kurt Rinck** / 17th January 2005.

Kurt stood still as I admired my License to Live. I had tears in my eyes as I reached out to Kurt and held his hand tight.

"It was a pleasure knowing you. If you need any help, you know how to reach me. I don't know if I will have all the answers but I do know I can put you on an assignment to get them for yourself," Kurt burst into laughter as he stretched out his hand and held me close.

"Have you heard of the genie inside the magic lamp?" he asked as he began to walk me towards the car.

"Yes." I had read stories about the magic lamp, how a genie lived inside it and when Aladdin rubbed the magic lamp, the genie emerged and granted Aladdin his wishes.

"What you don't know is that YOU are the genie!" Kurt said, suddenly stopping and looking directly at me. "YOU are the GENIE trapped inside a stupid lamp waiting for someone to come and rub you right so you can emerge and get a glimpse of your greatness for a short while and then hide back inside the lamp. YOU are that BIG genie inside that LITTLE lamp!" Kurt shook my shoulder as if waking me up from deep sleep.

"Wake up! Realize that the magic is in you. The power lies with you; the power to grant yourself the wishes you deserve. Stop hiding. Stop wasting your time and your life waiting for people to discover you. You are the genie the world is waiting for. When you emerge, you empower others to emerge too. We don't need another lamp to light the world. There is electricity for Christ's sake. We need you to wake up to your true self! Do you understand?" Kurt almost barked in my face.

"Your learning, your journey, and your knowing is for you. I don't need it. I don't even need to hear it. I see your change and your evolution in the light that radiates from you. And as long as you can keep yourself out of the lamp, into present time, I know that your world will be safe and you will keep it safe for others too. I know you will shine because you were meant to. I know that others will shine in your presence because you can't but help that. I know I am proud to have you as a part of my journey and I know I am happy that I could help." Kurt let go of my hand as he walked still looking at me. "My knowing all of this is not enough. What will change your life is when YOU KNOW all that I KNOW about you!"

"In these seven days I never taught you a thing. I was not even there with you. YOU found your own knowing. How can you recognize the truth if you don't know it to be true first? How can you learn a 'lesson' if you don't already know it to be of value to your life first? How can you be lost if you lead yourself out of your confusion in the first place? You have known yourself all along, you just have been afraid of your own greatness. Like the genie you get a glimpse of your enormity and greatness but because there are other Aladdins who pretend to rule over you, you hide back into the little lamp." Kurt took his finger and bopped me on the head just like Bomo had done and it stung. "Wake up," he said. "You know your destiny. Create it!"

"Have a good life!" Kurt waved as he left me standing on the seaway. My feet were stuck to the ground. Kurt's words had frozen me. I watched him get into the car, take a turn and speed off. I stood there staring at the dot the car now looked like until it totally disappeared into the distance.

I opened my palm where I held the diamond ring. Something made me turn around and walk back to the ledge. This is where I regularly came since a long time. I stood at the same spot, my 'lost spot'. The place where I used to come for answers, and always went back emptier. It was the same place, but I was no longer lost. I had found myself. And I knew that everywhere I went, I would carry the liberated genie in me. All my questions had only one answer: 'Responsibility'. No matter how bad or confusing life may become, if I could just take responsibility for one tiny part of it, I could change the world, my world to begin with. I felt happy and I felt free, and that was all that mattered. I knew that from this place of freedom I would create a magical future. I stared at the horizon and my life was lit with meaning. The sky had changed colors and I stood spellbound as I witnessed the first sign of daybreak. It was as though the universe had let me in on its magic.

I began to walk towards the car. I had had the greatest adventure of my life. I knew that my life from here would be beautiful because I knew how to create it. I knew the genie had emerged because I honestly felt free. I opened the door of my car and sat inside. And as I shut the door I took one look at the ring gleaming in the morning light. I knew one helluva future was waiting for me. I knew that I could be, do, and have anything I ever wanted. The lamp had been rubbed and destroyed forever; the genie was free! I knew it!

I took the ring and as I was slipping it on my finger a small engraving on the edge caught my eye. It had seemed like a design earlier but right now I thought I caught a glimpse of a word. I tilted the ring and squinted to read the engraving. Suddenly, a ray of sunlight lit up the ring in one magical moment and I could see the very small letters engraved on the side of the ring: '*Sam loves Priya*'.

"Sam!" I exclaimed as I hastily looked around. Kurt was long gone and I was there alone. My journey into a blessed future had already begun!!

ALSO BY PRIYA KUMAR

"A Journey to Powerful Breakthroughs"

#1 BEST SELLER

I AM
another
YOU

by priya kumar

Price: Rs.195/-

A book of many lessons, many insights and many truths, it has the power to awaken you to your best self and above all lead you to your own personal breakthroughs!

"With Priya, you journey through the pages, every page - an honest narration of struggle, overcoming and victory. This book will urge you to take that path you always knew was right but never had the courage to follow."

— *Times of India*

"In an honest narrative extracted from real life experience, the book takes the reader through struggle, overcoming and victory over self. It deals with breakthroughs that can be used by anyone to achieve personal success in the true sense of the word."

— *Gulf Today*

"I Am another YOU is a meditation on the power of human beings to transform themselves, if they so desire, and the testimony to the triumph of the human spirit against life-altering odds."

— *The Asian Age*

CONNECT WITH PRIYA:

You can connect with Priya Kumar on the following platforms :

1. Facebook : username : Priya Kumar

2. Twitter : http://twitter.com/kumarpriya

3. Blogger : http://iamanotheryouthebook.blogspot.com

4. Website : www.priya-kumar.com

5. Email : priyasdesk@priya-kumar.com